The Policy Studies Institute (PSI) is one of Europe's leading independent research organisations undertaking studies of economic, industrial and social policy, and the workings of political institutions.

PSI is a registered charity, run on a non-profit basis, and is not associated with any political party, pressure group or commercial interest.

PSI attaches great importance to covering a wide range of subject areas with its multi-disciplinary approach. The Institute's researchers are organised in groups which currently cover the following programmes:

Crime, Justice and Youth Studies – *Employment and Society* – *Ethnic Equality and Diversity* – *European Industrial Development* – *Family Finances* – *Information and Citizenship* – *Information and Cultural Studies* – *Social Care and Health Studies* – *Work, Benefits and Social Participation*

This publication arises from the Ethnic Equality and Diversity group and is one of over 30 publications made available by the Institute each year.

Information about the work of PSI and a catalogue of available books can be obtained from:

External Relations Department, PSI
100 Park Village East, London NW1 3SR

Nursing in a Multi-Ethnic NHS

Sharon Beishon, Satnam Virdee and Ann Hagell

POLICY STUDIES INSTITUTE
London

PUBLISHING

**The publishing imprint of the independent
POLICY STUDIES INSTITUTE
100 Park Village East, London NW1 3SR
Telephone: 0171 468 0468   Fax: 0171 388 0914**

The views expressed in this report are those of the authors and not necessarily those of
the Department of Health or any other Government organisation or department.

ISBN 0 85374 662 1

PSI Research Report 775

A CIP catalogue record of this book is available from the British Library.

1 2 3 4 5 6 7 8 9

PSI publications are available from
BEBC Distribution Ltd
P O Box 1496, Poole, Dorset, BH12 3YD

Books will normally be despatched within 24 hours. Cheques should be made payable
to BEBC Distribution Ltd.

Credit card and telephone/fax orders may be placed on the following freephone
numbers:

FREEPHONE: 0800 262260
FREEFAX: 0800 262266

Booktrade Representation (UK & Eire):
Broadcast Books
24 De Montfort Road, London SW16 1LZ
Telephone: 0181 769 3483   Answerphone / fax: 0181 677 5129

PSI subscriptions are available from PSI's subscription agent
Carfax Publishing Company Ltd
P O Box 25, Abingdon, Oxford OX14 3UE

Laserset by Policy Studies Institute
Printed in Great Britain by BPC Books and Journals Ltd, Exeter

Contents

Tables

Figures

Acknowledgements

This book results from a project commissioned by the Department of Health on nursing and midwifery staff in a multi-ethnic society, and was carried out between 1992 and 1994. It is part of a major programme of research conducted at PSI over the past two decades on aspects of the lives of Britain's ethnic minority populations. It also relates directly to a separate programme of work at PSI on progress in the medical profession.

We are grateful to the Department of Health for providing the financial support, and to the members of the advisory group for support and guidance, especially the Chair, Dr Elizabeth Meerabeau. The members represented a range of organisations including the Department of Health, the Mersey Regional Health Authority, the Applied Social Science Department at the University of Plymouth, the Royal College of Midwives, the Royal College of Nursing, the Commission for Racial Equality, Unison, the Health Visitor's Association, the UKCC, the Nursing Studies Department at the University of Hull, and Anglia Polytechnic University. David Smith (now of the University of Edinburgh) was largely responsible for the initial research design while still at PSI, and Richard Berthoud took his place as project manager on his departure.

We would like to thank Martin Bonell, Raj Guzadhur and all the staff at Barnet Psychiatric Unit. Thanks also to Sister Helen May and her staff at St. Bartholomew's for their help in the initial stages of this project. In addition, we owe a large debt to the literally thousands of people who have helped over the last two years. We are particularly grateful to the 14,330 nursing and midwifery staff who conscientiously completed the questionnaire, and also to others in the NHS who assisted in its distribution. We are also indebted to the nurse employers in the six case study areas for providing access for the project, and to the many employees who agreed to be interviewed and gave so generously of their time. Many thanks to Marion Kumar for undertaking many of the interviews with nursing staff in four of the six case study areas.

As always, a range of colleagues at PSI have contributed valuable help and support, especially Nick Evans, Rita Goldberg, Esther Lane and Siân Putnam.

PART I

BACKGROUND

1 Nursing and the NHS: overview and context

Nurses and midwifery staff belonging to ethnic minority groups have a long history of representation in the British National Health Service (NHS), in all its various incarnations. However, despite two decades of equal opportunities legislation (particularly the Race Relations Act 1976), various recent reports, anecdotal information, and media accounts all continue to suggest that racial inequality remains a significant problem in the NHS.

This study arose when the Department of Health invited the Policy Studies Institute (PSI) to submit a proposal for research into the experiences of nursing and midwifery staff belonging to ethnic minority groups in the NHS. PSI conducted a large research project comprising two main parts. The first was a qualitative study of six case study nurse employers. The second was a nationally representative postal survey of nursing and midwifery staff. The research was intended to address five main aims, the first three relating to the case studies, the last two to the postal survey:

- to identify how far NHS employers provide detailed guidelines for equal opportunities in recruitment, training, appraisal and flexible working, and to establish the extent to which these are followed in practice;

- to find out how far these policies and practices relate to the experiences of nursing and midwifery staff at all levels, and in particular to the experiences of ethnic minority nursing and midwifery staff;

- to examine the extent of racial harassment in the workplace as an issue for ethnic minority nursing and midwifery staff and to look at how they cope in the face of any harassment that might exist;

- to provide a picture of the progress and experiences of a representative sample of people working as nursing and midwifery staff in the NHS, and, finally

• to support detailed comparisons between members of ethnic minorities and others in terms of career progress.

In broad terms, the purpose of the research was to provide the framework of fact and analysis within which decisions could be made about how best to meet any needs identified.

The case studies covered the general issue of personnel policy and practice in the NHS and investigated whether the existing procedures were such that would allow fairness or which could lead to discrimination. Equality of opportunity and employment conditions for ethnic minority nursing and midwifery staff have to be assessed in the light of the broader personnel policy and practices for National Health Service (NHS) nurses as a whole. In general, personnel policy and practice should ensure that the best candidate for the job is selected, and that staff are sufficiently supported in their work, so that rates of turnover are low and levels of personal development are high. Service standards will be linked to general staff policies and practices. The qualitative approach undertaken in this part of the project was particularly important in investigating aspects of the problem in more detail. In-depth qualitative research of the type described in this book provides material concerning the range of policies, practices and experiences within the case study areas. Although it is unwise to draw firm statistical conclusions about the issues from qualitative research, it does provide an understanding of process which quantitative methods cannot.

The postal survey collected career history information on a nationally representative sample of over 14,000 nursing and midwifery staff, to complement the qualitative data collected in the case study areas. The survey included details about the current post; reports of relations with colleagues and patients; information from nursing and midwifery staff about opportunities for training and career development, equal opportunities and experience of racial discrimination and harassment.

The early 1990s have been a period of administrative change and reorganisation within the NHS, and the PSI programme of research has to be viewed in the context of the changing and evolving NHS. Policies and practices are necessarily wedded to the wider organisational framework, and in particular they are affected by the evolution of more localised management structure: the qualitative case studies need to be read in this general context. The postal survey, on the other hand, concentrated particularly on progression in the nursing professions, which itself is changing all the time. As part of the NHS changes, the situation and working conditions of all nursing and midwifery staff have been subject to restructuring, and this, together with the variety of qualifications possible and existence of different routes into the nursing professions, makes comparisons between nursing staff relatively difficult. As a background, the next sections outline the main features of the NHS organisational structuring and nursing and midwifery careers at the time the research took place, in 1994.

The current state of the NHS

The NHS, Britain's national healthcare service, has been reorganised approximately five times since its inception in 1948. These reorganisations began with the National Health Service Act in 1974, and culminated in the October 1993 decision to abolish the regional tier of management and merge District Health Authorities (DHAs) and Family Health Service Authorities (FHSAs). The reorganisations can be organised into three main blocks relating to three main decades of change to date: the 1970s and the development of consensus management; the 1980s and the introduction of general management; and the 1990s and the internal market.

The 1974 reorganisation aimed to unify health services, to encourage better coordination between health authorities and related government services, and to develop better management through the development of multi-disciplinary teams which would operate a model of consensus management. Briefly, the regional tier of RHAs had responsibility for strategic management, and the lower tier of Area Health Authorities (AHAs) was responsible for operational management. Below the AHAs were the DHAs, which were the smallest units for provision of full health services. These were sometimes at the level of a single hospital. Difficulties with the consensus model of management were quickly pointed out. Not having an explicit 'boss' who could take overall responsibility in the highly bureaucratic system, led to the delay and watering-down of decisions. Many participants and observers of the reorganisation felt that there were too many tiers and that this hindered good coordination. As Laing (1994: 11) comments:

> ... the 1974 reorganisation simply accepted the dominance of the medical profession in priority setting and decision making in the NHS and sought to create a more rational administrative structure under which the wide range of professional inputs might be co-ordinated in the interests of health care provision ... there remained an absence of any truly responsive levers of control. Even more so than today, the NHS could be likened to a super tanker which continued to move in the old direction long after the signal to turn had been given.

The early 1980s brought further reform. A team headed by Sir Roy Griffiths was set up to examine the effective use of management and manpower in the NHS. Consensus teams at district level had led to a lack of clearly defined general management. The final report did not criticise the structure, but the style of management then prevalent. The report recommended strong, general management for the NHS which could be achieved by appointing general managers at all levels. The government implemented the findings by ensuring that Health Authorities appointed general managers at all levels by the end of 1985. The introduction of general management for the first time created a clear line of accountability throughout the NHS. It represented a decisive shift from the old collegiate system of consensus management, and introduced business principles into NHS management style. The 1980s saw a strong move to limit the autonomy of professional groups and clinicians, and the aim of more effective management was to increase efficiency.

The late 1980s saw confrontation between the NHS management and the various healthcare professions, particularly nurses and GPs. In 1988, nurses working in the NHS were regraded, which was intended to create a system of nurse grading which was more amenable to general management. For the present study, the regrading provides particular problems in assessing career progression for nurses over the last few years.

In addition to pressures to increase efficiency, the late 1980s saw increasing financial pressure on the NHS. Budgetary limits could not keep up with the spiralling cost of health demands. In 1987 a cash crisis occurred in which hospitals were forced to take extreme measures to avoid spending in excess of their allotted budget. The media spotlight and the clamouring of professional medical bodies assisted the government view that spending on health required further evaluation. In January 1988 Mrs Thatcher announced a 'root and branch' Ministerial Review of the NHS. The review reported its results in the White Paper, Working for Patients (HMSO 1989), the proposals of which were incorporated into the NHS and Community Care Bill 1990.

A radical change in the delivery of health services was thus proposed with the introduction of an 'internal market'. The role of the purchaser of health care was to be separated from the role of the provider of health care. Where there had been line management relations between the tiers, there would now be contractual arrangements. District Health Authorities would be the purchasers for their communities and the hospitals and opted-out related health services (trusts) would be the providers. The relationship between purchasers and providers would be based solely on contracts and service agreements. Money would follow patients, with good services being rewarded with larger contracts. The introduction of

Figure 1.1   Structure of the NHS - 1993 (adapted from Laing 1994)

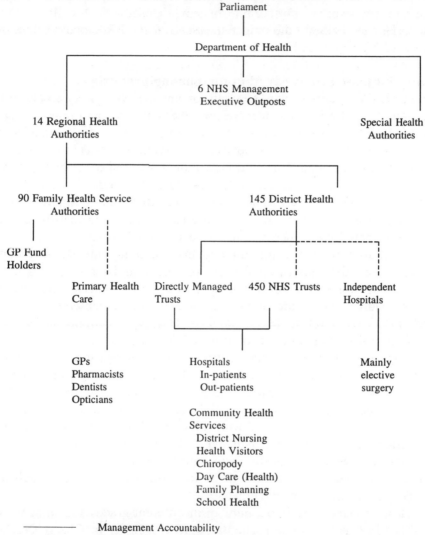

Parliament

Department of Health

6 NHS Management
Executive Outposts

14 Regional Health
Authorities

Special Health
Authorities

90 Family Health Service
Authorities

145 District Health
Authorities

GP Fund
Holders

Primary Health
Care

Directly Managed
Trusts

450 NHS Trusts

Independent
Hospitals

GPs
Pharmacists
Dentists
Opticians

Hospitals
In-patients
Out-patients

Community Health
Services
  District Nursing
  Health Visitors
  Chiropody
  Day Care (Health)
  Family Planning
  School Health

Mainly
elective
surgery

——————   Management Accountability
--------------   Contractual Accountability

competition, it was held, would make the health service more efficient and sensitive to patient needs.

Figure 1.1, which is adapted from a recent Office of Health Economics report (Laing 1994), illustrates the structure of the NHS in 1993 and early 1994, at the time when this study was being conducted. It shows the lines of management and contractual accountability between the various tiers. The 90 FHSAs and 145 DHAs are the main purchasers

7

(with funds allocated by the RHAs above them), buying services from the Trusts, directly managed units, primary health care providers and independent hospitals. Further reforms are proposed, which will integrate the DHAs and FHSAs, and reduce the 14 RHAs to 8 Regional Offices of the NHS Management Executive.

Entry into and progress within the nursing professions

The United Kingdom Central Council for Nursing, Midwifery and Health Visiting (UKCC) has statutory responsibility for the minimum educational requirements for entry to nurse training. Currently these include 5 GCSE passes at Grade C or above, or their equivalent. This was raised from 2 in 1986, to standardise the educational requirements. Other means of entry are based on an equivalent academic standard. Beyond these minimum requirements, various colleges of nursing and midwifery may set their own entry requirements. There is some concern that there is a lack of standard guidelines beyond those set by the UKCC.

For those without the minimum educational requirements, entry may be achieved through three further routes. The first is to take an educational test (the 'DC test'), approved by the UKCC. Secondly, access courses which are approved for entry to higher education are recognised for entry to nurse training. Thirdly, vocational and other qualifications can provide a further means for entry.

Until recently, nurses were either trained as Registered Nurses or Enrolled Nurses. The latter had a shorter training. Most registered nurses trained as RGNs (Registered General Nurses) but there were also separate courses as RMNs (Registered Mental Nurses), RNMHs (Registered Nurses for the Mentally Handicapped) and RSCNs (Registered Sick Children's Nurses). It is possible for nurses to take 'conversion courses' to transfer from Enrolled to Registered Nurse. Many nurses take post-registration courses in particular specialties, such as cancer nursing or care of the elderly.

Hospital nurses fall into a number of different grades and categories. The head of nursing on a particular ward is a Sister or Charge Nurse, although these are now increasingly called Ward Managers. Under her there will be qualified Staff Nurses as well as Student Nurses. Nurse Managers are responsible for nursing staff on a number of wards, in a unit or hospital. Some hospitals have introduced the concept of primary nursing, where each patient is assigned their 'own nurse', who is particularly responsible for their care.

Other nursing-related staff in hospitals and community practices include those who are unqualified. Nursing Auxiliaries, who may have an auxiliary certificate of some kind but who are unqualified as nurses, help with duties such as bathing and meals on wards. In addition, there are nursing assistants, and health care assistants.

Community nurses offer services to people living in the community, and work with GPs, social workers, health professionals, chiropodists, etc. They work in a variety of settings including health centres, GP surgeries, schools and the workplace. They include district nurses, health visitors, practice nurses, school nurses, community psychiatric nurses and other specialist nurses. These have all completed further training as well as their basic nursing qualification.

Midwives are practitioners in their own right and are allowed to prescribe certain drugs without the sanction of a doctor. Most midwives are registered general nurses who then go on to do a specialist midwifery qualification. However, it is possible to qualify as a midwife without training as a nurse first. In 1992/1993, 16 per cent of entrants to midwifery qualifying courses were not registered nurses. The trend is for a growing proportion to come via this route. Midwives practice in both hospitals and the community.

The 1988 regrading introduced nursing grades A – I. It is assumed that all nurses graded D and above are registered nurses, and that all those graded C are enrolled (Department of Health 1991), although it is known that an unidentified number of enrolled nurses are graded D and above. There are also many enrolled nurses with additional qualifications or responsibilities, such as those with post-basic certificates or those who supervise other staff. In 1989, the proportion of all nursing and midwifery staff who were qualified nurses, midwives and health visitors was over 61 per cent. Staff in grades D and E represent over 50 per cent of all qualified staff.

Some of the complications inherent in the nursing professions, such as the two tiers of entry, are being ironed out with the introduction of Project 2000, which is creating one level of trained nurse at a minimum of diploma level. Recruitment to the second level enrolled nurse qualification, or to the first level state registered nurse qualification, has ceased as Project 2000 is adopted. Meanwhile, nurses may continue to convert their second level qualification to first level standard by obtaining conversion training. It should be emphasised that this description of nursing qualifications is the situation as it applied to most of the nurses in the cohort under study, but the registered/enrolled distinction no longer actually applies with the introduction of Project 2000.

Against this general background on entry to the nursing professions, the specific issue of entry by ethnic minority nurses has been a feature of the NHS for the last three decades. Ethnic minority nurses in the NHS fall into two main categories, (a) those who were recruited directly from overseas, and (b) those who were born or largely brought up in the UK and were recruited through the same procedures as white indigenous nurses. Overseas recruitment brought not only black nurses to the UK but also white nurses, particularly of Irish origin. As a rule, where we refer to overseas ethnic minority nurses, we are making reference to those who are not white.

Considering first those who were recruited from overseas, large numbers of ethnic minority nurses moved to the UK to train in the 1960s and 1970s. This was the result of what an earlier survey referred to as 'a marriage of convenience', as the early 1960s saw both a chronic shortage of nurses in British hospitals, and the existence at the same time of many Commonwealth citizens who wanted to enter Britain to train and live (Thomas and Morton-Williams 1972). The number of overseas nurses recruited reached a peak in 1970. By 1971, there were over 15,000 overseas student nurses, of whom 40 per cent were West Indians, 29 per cent Asian and 27 per cent African (Akinsanya 1988). Although very few reliable statistics exist about the numbers of NHS staff born overseas, separate studies on doctors and nurses suggest certain proportions. A study by the Social and Community Planning Research institute for the Briggs Committee in the early 1970s suggested that overseas nurses formed 9 per cent of the hospital nursing population (Morton-Williams and Berthoud 1971b). Half of these were from the West Indies, a quarter from Africa and a quarter from Asia (Thomas and Morton-Williams 1972). In 1980, PSI supplemented these figures by publishing a report on overseas doctors in the NHS (Smith 1980), which stated that, according to a survey of 2,000 doctors, 38 per cent were born overseas. Since the late 1970s, the numbers are generally held to be declining.

As Baxter (1988) reports, the 1971 Immigration Act and the introduction of work permits meant that nurses from the Commonwealth ceased to have any automatic right to enter the country and made it considerably more difficult to recruit from overseas. By 1983, work permits had been withdrawn and the need for cheap labour declined, and by the mid-1980s entry into the nursing professions directly from overseas had virtually ceased.

Ethnic minority nurses are still being recruited, of course, and the second category of ethnic minority nurses are those who were born in this country. This reflects the increasingly multi-ethnic nature of the UK in the late 20th century. These nurses are exposed and, we assume, respond in the same way as their white counterparts to the general recruitment drive of the NHS in schools, the national press, career and job centres. Whether the NHS then responds to them in exactly the same way has been strongly questioned and is, of course, the central focus of this book.

The number of ethnic minority nurses in the 1990s

Evidence relating to numbers of ethnic minority nurses is, at present, fragmentary because a system for regularly monitoring the ethnic origins of applicants and staff is not yet in place. From April 1990, the English National Board (ENB), which operates the Nurses Central Clearing House, started collecting data on the ethnic origins of recruits to basic training. The UKCC, which is responsible for the registration of qualified nurses, has made the decision to collect data on the ethnic origin of newly registered nurses, but it may be some years before they have information about the ethnic origins of all nurses on the register. There is, as yet, little in the way of clear commitment by the employers (district health authorities, trusts and agencies) to keep ethnic records of their nursing and midwifery staff. Hence, over the next few years, systematic information about the position of ethnic minorities in nursing can only be provided by systematic research studies, or from existing data bases on Britain's ethnic minorities in the workforce.

Several early studies on overseas recruits to the NHS have been discussed above, including the Social and Community Planning Research (SCPR) survey conducted for the Briggs Committee, and the PSI study on doctors. Both of these suggest fairly high proportions of overseas nurses and doctors in the 1970s, but only refer to ethnic minority nurses born abroad. Some reliable and more recent estimates of the numbers of ethnic minorities in the workforce, including those born here, are available from the Labour Force Survey. Table 1.1 gives the Labour Force Survey figures for representation of various ethnicities in the nursing professions in Great Britain, for the years 1988-1990. The figures for each year were aggregated, producing about 5,000 men and 3,500 women who were in work and who belonged to ethnic minority groups. The size of the sample allows for confidence that the figures are reasonably accurate.

The table shows how the nursing workforce is distributed between ethnic groups. Thus, 6.3 per cent of female nurses belonged to ethnic minority groups in this sample, compared with 3.6 of all females in employment; while 14.7 per cent of male nurses belonged to ethnic minority groups, compared with 3.9 per cent of all males in employment.

Table 1.1   Ethnic minorities in nursing in Great Britain, from the Labour Force Survey 1988-1990

| | Percentage belonging to each ethnic group | | | |
| Ethnicity | Men | | Women | |
	All	Nurses	All	Nurses
White	95.3	83.4	95.6	92.6
Total ethnic minorities	3.9	14.7	3.6	6.3
West Indian	0.8	3.0	1.0	3.4
African Asian	0.4	0.1	0.3	0.3
Indian	1.0	3.3	0.9	0.6
Pakistani	0.5	-	0.2	-
Bangladeshi	0.1	-	-	-
Chinese	0.2	1.7	0.2	0.6
African	0.2	2.6	0.2	0.6
Other or mixed	0.6	3.9	0.5	1.0
Ethnic group not known	0.7	1.1	0.7	0.8

If all ethnic minorities are grouped together, therefore, the findings show that the ethnic minorities are substantially over-represented in nursing.

The table also shows large differences between specific ethnic groups. Groups that were strongly over-represented in nursing are people of West Indian, Chinese, African and of 'other or mixed' origin. Groups that were under-represented were people of Indian, Pakistani, Bangladeshi and African Asian origin – in other words, all south Asian groups. Representation in nursing was lowest among people of Pakistani and Bangladeshi origin, nearly all of whom are Muslims. In fact, three years of the Labour Force Survey did not turn up a single Pakistani or Bangladeshi respondent who was working as a nurse. Economic activity is in any case substantially lower among Muslim women than among females belonging to other groups; also the level of educational qualifications tends to be low among Muslim women in Britain, most of whom did not pass through the British educational system. These factors would not be enough to explain the virtual or total absence of Muslim women in nursing, and other specific explanations need to be sought.

The experiences of ethnic minorities in the nursing professions

Despite its fragmentary nature, commentary on discrimination against racial minorities in the health professions has been ongoing since the first ethnic minority workers first joined the professions. In 1857, a black nurse called Mary Seacole reported how differently she was treated from her white colleagues (see Alexander and Dewjee 1984). The NHS desperately needed staff in the 1960s and 1970s and recruited strenuously from overseas groups, but having done so seemed for years to show a remarkable reluctance to acknowledge the essentially different nature of their experiences within the health service they helped to underpin. As one recent commentator suggests, this avoidance of the issue seemed to have been taken as tacit acceptance of the absence of a problem of racial discrimination in the service (Akinsanya 1988).

However, recently things have begun to change and the commentary is becoming more than fragmentary. An increasing amount of interest has been focused on the role and experiences of ethnic minority nurses in the last few years, and the UKCC has started to address the issue. As mentioned above, both the ENB and the UKCC have recently started to collect more information on ethnicity of recruits to training. The development of equal opportunities policies by nurse employers is ongoing and the NHS Training Authority (now part of the NHSE Personnel Directorate) has taken on training projects directed specifically at race issues.[1] The imperatives for the NHS to concentrate resources and energy on the issue are severalfold and include the importance of reflecting the multi-ethnic society in which it functions, particularly as care in the community becomes more common. However, as Baxter (1988: 8) writes:

> The endurance of black nurses has been tested more cruelly and far longer, by persistent and systematic racism in the NHS, and the long-running haemorrhage of their commitment and skill, which the NHS can ill afford to lose, will not be staunched until positive measures are taken to eliminate racism in this, the most avowedly caring of professions.

In addition to the PEP and PSI surveys reporting the numbers of ethnic minority nurses and doctors, several smaller scale, qualitative studies and reports have reported aspects of their experiences, although the data are impressionistic and the projects very small scale. In 1983 the

---

1   Training in Health and Race, 1982-1987, first funded by the Health Education Authority and the Department of Health, and from 1987, part of the NHS Training Authority. The project aims to work towards a health service more responsive to the needs of a multi-ethnic society. See, for details, Baxter (1988).

Commission for Racial Equality (CRE) published a short report on ethnic minority hospital staff (CRE 1983). In their report, the CRE set out to investigate the claim by health authority administrators and personnel officers that the lack of discrimination in the health service was evidenced by the fact that a large number of ethnic minority staff were employed. This was taken by the CRE to be a non sequitur, and examples were given of unlawful discrimination. There were various areas for serious concern. One of these was the question of concentration of certain specialties, and it appeared that black nurses were more likely to be found within specialties such as geriatrics and mental illness. These areas were less popular and tended to be less academic, although they were better paid to attract people to them. Concluding their brief survey of existing literature, the CRE claimed that the hospital service is as vulnerable to unlawful discrimination as other employers. The report also distinguished between individual discrimination which was the result of isolated behaviour by one person, and more institutionalised discrimination where the 'unthinking operation of a system' discriminated against ethnic minority groups as a whole.

One qualitative study a few years later (Baxter 1988) was based on interviews with 32 minority ethnicity nurses (both British and overseas born) and one white British nurse, most of whom were living and working in the Manchester area. From these interviews, Baxter concluded that black nurses experienced particular difficulties at all stages of their careers, from recruitment and deployment through to promotion. The nurses felt isolated and helpless, partly due to a perceived lack of support from their training schools or by their professional organisations.

The general themes of the various reports and studies were drawn together in a review article in the late 1980s by Professor Akinsanya, now of Anglia Polytechnic University. Based on a report prepared for the CRE, Akinsanya's review emphasised again the central problem: the high numbers of ethnic minority nurses in second level recruitment; the over-representation of such nurses in unpopular or lower grade specialties; the low numbers of ethnic minority nurses in the higher grades after the reorganisation of the nursing grades; the general lack of opportunity for personal and professional development.

Reinforcing these conclusions, in 1990 the King's Fund Equal Opportunities Task Force published a position paper on racial inequality in the nursing profession (Ellis 1990), which again concluded that 'racial inequality in the nursing profession is wide ranging and deep seated' (para 15.1). This statement was not, however, based on any new research.

It referred to a CRE survey published in 1987 which showed that ethnic minority trainees were under-represented in certain training schools, though not in others. It also referred to the evidence in a couple of districts that ethnic minority nurses were concentrated in more junior grades and in less popular specialties, such as geriatrics and mental illness. Thus, 'a CRE formal investigation of a unit of South Manchester health authority, published in 1988, found that black nurses constituted 29 per cent of applicants for promotion but only 8 per cent of those successful' (para 2.3), although the CRE found no unlawful discrimination.

The Kings Fund report outlined a number of main areas of concern. In summary, a major worry continues to be that, according to the existing piecemeal and anecdotal information, in the light of their length of service in the profession black and ethnic minority nurses are under-represented in senior positions as well as in teaching hospitals and acute units. Supporting this theory, a series of industrial tribunal cases have been brought by ethnic minority nurses, concerning discrimination in career development issues.

A series of concerns has been expressed about access to training opportunities and to various steps up the nursing ladder. The Kings Fund report suggested that ethnic minority nurses are experiencing discrimination in that training opportunities are not made equally available to all nurses. Selection to basic and post-basic training, promotion and career development opportunities are all open to the suspicion that the criteria at every level are not clear, adhered to or objective.

Finally, racial abuse and harassment at work is another area of serious concern (Virdee 1995). As an issue, it has been asserted that this largely goes unrecognised by management. Policies for dealing with racial abuse by other staff and by patients need to be clearly implemented, and research is needed to establish the extent and nature of racial abuse both by other staff and by patients.

Main research questions and aims

This brief review highlights several main areas of concern which form the central issue that this book will seek to address. In response, the two parts of the study sought to provide a comprehensive analysis of the training opportunities, promotional opportunities, appraisal procedures and general experiences of ethnic minority nurses and midwives. The experiences of ethnic minority nurses have to be viewed against the background of the general organisational structure of the NHS, and their general career development has to be seen in the light of that of nurses and midwives generally. The study covers the extent to which NHS employers have clearly defined equal opportunities criteria, and the extent to which such policies work in the new environment of the internal market. Is selection and promotion conducted according to clearly explicit and formal criteria, and how do these criteria work in practice? How does policy work to protect and develop the potential of various minority groups? How does staff appraisal work or not work?

Within the nursing professions, the actual representation of ethnic minority nurses seems relatively high, given the Labour Force Survey data, but are they under-represented in the higher grades? Or do they work in particular specialties which might strategically limit their access to promotion and further career development? The existing division between registered and enrolled nurses is thought to have implications for equal opportunities, particularly with the introduction of Project 2000 and a single level training. It is thought that black and ethnic minority nurses are concentrated in the C and possibly D grades (equivalent to the previous classification of being enrolled) and, although conversion courses are becoming more accessible and length of training required for conversion is being relaxed, the availability of conversion courses remains limited. There is evidence that the wide variety of paths to conversion are not being used to full advantage, and it is believed that, because they are already thought to be concentrated in the EN grade (or equivalent), ethnic minority nurses have less access to conversion and thus to the higher grades. Is there any evidence that this is the case? Do the appraisal and promotional procedures show signs of institutional discrimination against ethnic minority groups?

The *qualitative study of six case study areas* had the following aims:

* The first was to study policies and practices within the National Health Service as they affected opportunities for ethnic minority nurses. What steps have already been taken to secure equal opportunities and what difficulties have arisen in implementing these measures? Could any constructive suggestions for future practice be made based on an analysis of what is already being done?

* The second was to provide a detailed description of the experience, views, and attitudes of white and ethnic minority nurses on a wide range of issues, in order to complement the more limited but quantitative information that was provided by the postal survey.

The major issues addressed within each of the case study areas were as follows:

- Recruitment and selection. Recruitment has to be the starting point upon which the ability of each NHS employer to deliver its particular service will rest. Assumptions and stereotypes about ethnic minority groups can affect selection decisions.

- Effective staff review systems, such as appraisal procedures, are vital for individual staff development and for the development of the employer. In practice these range from non-existent to very formalised, and the degree of flexibility and formality may have implications for nursing and midwifery staff from ethnic minority backgrounds.

- Training opportunities are an issue of increasing importance in the NHS, particularly in the face of limited resources. The need to undertake further training is very strong for nursing and midwifery staff who wish to progress, and limitations on access to training will affect equal opportunities.

- General equal opportunities policies may be formalised statements or more informal guidelines. In each case study area, policy documents were assessed in terms of their clarity, comprehensiveness and direction.

- Flexible working arrangements are a significant consideration for an employer whose workforce is largely female, particularly in terms of staff retention. Flexible working hours give employees more choice, but should not lead to discrimination in terms of promotion opportunities.

- Relationships with colleagues and patients. The extent to which ethnic minority nursing staff feel discriminated against within the NHS and their actual experience of racial harassment and discrimination while working for the NHS. The way ethnic minority staff are treated by their patients, nursing colleagues and managers will influence their attitude not only to their job, but to nursing and the NHS as a whole.

The *postal survey* set out to answer these specific questions:

- Who comprises the NHS nursing and midwifery staff, and how are they placed within the NHS?

- What is the current distribution of ethnic minority nursing and midwifery staff across grades and specialty?

- What are the reasons for any differences in this pattern?

- What differences are there in the progress of ethnic minority nursing and midwifery staff compared to white nursing staff?

Decisions were made regarding the types of nursing staff who would be included in the research. Primarily, it was decided to concentrate on permanent staff. Second, a decision was made to exclude nursing staff who were bank staff (working as agency nurses for the NHS) but who did not have permanent nursing positions. Students were excluded. These decisions have implications for the representativeness of the samples in terms of the general nursing population, and fairly large proportions of nursing staff are not permanent. However, it was decided to include unqualified auxiliary staff (so long as they had permanent positions) in order to make comparisons between ethnic origin at all the grading levels.

The coverage of the study

The study took a deliberately broad view of what groups of staff should be covered. A narrow view of 'nursing' involves trained and qualified people undertaking technical or caring activities in a hospital setting. However, the study also includes auxiliary staff who have not been trained to do 'real' nursing. We also include midwives and health visitors, who by the narrow definition are no longer really nurses. (Indeed, a sixth of midwives have had no initial training as nurses.)

The study therefore covers nursing and allied activities, rather than nursing in its narrowest sense. Auxiliaries, midwives and health visitors were included in both surveys. Where it is important to distinguish between different types of activity, we make this clear. However, in general, the terms 'nurse', 'nursing' and 'nursing staff' are used in their broad meaning, and cover all the types of staff covered by the study.

2 Method of research

Methods: The case studies

Sampling

The case studies were undertaken within six district health authorities and trusts in the NHS which employed nursing and midwifery staff. In order to ensure the six nurse employers selected accurately reflected both the geographical distribution of the ethnic minority population and the geographical spread of the ethnic minority nursing workforce in England, a two-stage process of selection was undertaken.

First, the 1988-1990 Labour Force Survey data was used to calculate the appropriate ethnic minority population and ethnic minority nursing workforce sizes within each region. From this it was found that the four regions with the highest population concentration of ethnic minorities were the following:

- *The South East region including Greater London* While 54 per cent of the total ethnic minority population were resident in the South East region, over 60 per cent of all ethnic minority nurses were working there. Concentrations were highest in the Greater London area, where 28 per cent of all nurses were of ethnic minority origin.

- *The West Midlands region* 14 per cent of the total ethnic minority population were resident and 15 per cent of all ethnic minority nurses were working within the region.

- *The North West region* Nine per cent of the total ethnic minority population were resident and 6 per cent of all ethnic minority nurses were working in the NW region. However, only 4 per cent of all nurses working within the region were of ethnic minority origin.

- *The East Midlands region* Six per cent of the total ethnic minority population were resident and 5 per cent of all ethnic minority nurses were working in the region. The data also showed that 5 per cent of all nurses in the East Midlands region were of ethnic minority origin.

To reflect both the distribution of the total ethnic minority population and the ethnic minority nursing workforce throughout England, it was decided that three of the six employers would be chosen from the South East region (including Greater London), and one each from the West Midlands, North West and East Midlands regions.

The second stage involved the selection of the most appropriate nurse employers within these four English regions. It was crucial to make sure that sufficient interviews could be undertaken with ethnic minority nurses within each of the selected nurse employers across a wide range of nursing specialties. In the absence of ethnic monitoring by most nurse employers within the NHS, a proxy of the total ethnic minority population had to be used to ensure that we selected nurse employers that would have substantial numbers of ethnic minority nurses in their workforce. Although clearly not ideal it did give us an indication of the possible ethnic minority nursing workforce within these nursing employers. An article by John Haskey (1991) in the OPCS Population

Table 2.1   Proportion of ethnic minority population in each case study area

Nurse employer	Ethnic minorities as per cent of general population
Case study A	11.1
Case study B	12.6
Case study C	14.7
Case study D	20.0
Case study E	19.1
Case study F	12.3

Source: Haskey 1991.

Note: Since April 1991, individual hospitals and community units which previously came under the responsibility of the district health authority have had the option of applying for self-governing status from the Department of Health. Due to the re-organisation currently being undertaken within the NHS, particularly with the institutionalisation of the purchaser/provider split and the move towards trust status, three of the nurse employers participating in the research changed their status from district health authorities to trusts in the course of the study. This caused great problems in gaining access because, where previously permission could have been granted by the chief executive of the district health authority, now many layers of management had to be approached. Two case studies became single trusts in 1993, and one split into several different trusts.

Trends Journal was used to provide more detailed information on the size of the ethnic minority population by metropolitan county and district. From this the six nurse employers selected were as follows.

Table 2.1 shows that ethnic minority groups represent at least 11 per cent of the general population in all six of the selected districts. Two case studies had high proportions of black people in their areas while all six nurse employers had substantial proportions of Asians.

The next stage entailed deciding what interviews were to be undertaken within each of the six nurse employers. The variables that needed to be taken into account when deciding this were ethnicity, gender, specialty and grade. If we were to be purely statistically representative of the distribution of nurses and midwives in the NHS in our selection of nurses within the case studies we would have been forced to interview a very small number of nurses in some of the smaller nursing specialties like paediatrics. This would not have proved to have been very worthwhile: it would not have allowed us to come to a clear understanding of the processes at work in determining nurses' chances of career development, especially because we would not have been able to interview nurses in a wide variety of grades within each specialty without increasing dramatically the number of interviews to be carried out with nursing and midwifery staff. Hence, in order to fulfil the objectives outlined for the case study areas it was necessary to concentrate the interviews with nursing and midwifery staff in a number of selected specialties. It was decided to concentrate the research on five nursing specialties and undertake a substantial number of interviews in each.

The five specialties selected were as follows:

• General nursing (both medical and surgical);

• Care of the elderly;

• Mental health;

• Midwifery and maternity;

• Community.

According to Department of Health statistics (Department of Health 1991) 94.5 per cent of all nursing and midwifery staff work in these five specialties. More important, these specialties were selected because past research has established that general nursing and community are areas of nursing where ethnic minority nursing and midwifery staff are under-represented, particularly above staff nurse level. On the other hand, it has been thought that ethnic minority staff have tended to be located in greater numbers in what have been regarded as the 'cinderella' nursing specialties such as mental health, and care of the elderly, although again in the lower grades. Consequently, selecting nurses for interview within these diverse areas of work enabled us to make a useful comparison of the problems facing nursing staff in a diverse range of specialties both where they were over-represented and under-represented.

Thus, interviews were undertaken in five nursing specialties across six nurse employers. Within each of the six nurse employers, interviews with nursing staff were undertaken in at least two different nursing specialties. In addition, between six and 12 interviews with nurses from the range of clinical nursing grades were carried out in each specialty within each nursing employer. As far as was possible, an attempt was made to ensure that significant numbers of ethnic minority nurses were interviewed across the range of grades and specialties in each of the six nurse employers.

Response rates and cooperation

Three of the originally selected nurse employers refused to cooperate – two of these because of NHS reorganisation and the other because they were just starting a review of their equal opportunity policies. It is likely that the latter refusal introduces a bias, since it seemed that management refused because they felt they had done little so far to implement an equal opportunity policy.

The first contact was made with the chief executive, but initial meetings were generally with senior nurses and personnel managers. Repeated contacts and meetings were needed to secure agreement to

Table 2.2   Schedule of interviews with management staff by employer and specialty

Employer	General nursing	Care of the elderly	Mental health	Midwifery	Community
A	3	–	3	–	3
B	–	3	–	3	3
C	–	3	–	3	–
D	3	–	–	3	–
E	–	3	–	–	3
F	3	–	3	–	–

Table 2.3   Schedule of interviews with nursing staff by employer and specialty

Employer	General nursing	Care of the elderly	Mental health	Midwifery	Community
A	6	–	8	–	6
B	–	6	–	6	6
C	–	10	–	10	–
D	10	–	–	8	–
E	–	8	–	–	12
F	8	–	10	–	–
Total number of interviews within each specialty	24	24	18	24	24

participate from the six nurse employers that took part. This entailed not only having to gain formal access from senior management but also from those ward managers where the research was scheduled to be undertaken.

Interviews were with both management staff in the six areas, and with practising nurses in each area. It was decided that in each specialty in all of the six case study areas, a total of three interviews would be carried out with management. These encompassed the ward manager in the ward where the nurse interviews were being undertaken, the personnel manager responsible for the particular specialty and the senior nurse or director of nursing services of the specialty. A total of 42 management interviews were undertaken in the six case study areas, as shown in Table 2.2.

In addition, Table 2.3 shows that a total of 114 interviews with qualified and unqualified nursing and midwifery staff were carried out across the six case study areas, in either two or three specialties in each. An attempt was made to ensure that the same number of ethnic minority and white nursing staff were interviewed in each employer. In the case of one employer, this proved to be impossible because of the scarcity of ethnic minority staff employed by the trust. Across the six employers, a total of 60 interviews were undertaken with white nursing staff and 54 with ethnic minority staff.

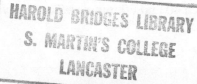

23

Table 2.4 shows that a total of 27 interviews were undertaken with unqualified nursing staff, 41 interviews with staff nurses, 44 interviews with sisters and ward managers, health visitors and district nurses and 4 interviews with senior nurses working in the community.

Table 2.4   Schedule of interviews of nursing staff by grade and specialty

Grade	General nursing	Care of the elderly	Mental health	Midwifery	Community
A and B	6	7	6	6	2
C, D and E	12	11	8	6	4
F and G	6	6	4	12	14
H and I	–	–	–	–	4

Interviewing procedures

The informal depth interviews that formed the core of the case studies were conducted in the nurses' working situation. First, interviews were conducted with three different layers of management, namely the ward manager or sister responsible for the particular ward where the interviews with nurses were undertaken, the personnel manager responsible for the particular specialty in question and the senior nurse or director of nursing services of the particular specialty. These interviews covered a range of themes including detailed investigation of the recruitment and selection procedure for the particular specialty, if and how staff appraisals were undertaken, on what basis were training opportunities allocated, the availability of childcare and flexible working arrangements and the measures undertaken to implement the employer's equal opportunity policy.

Secondly, a series of depth interviews were conducted using a semi-structured questionnaire with qualified and unqualified nursing staff, midwives, health visitors and district nurses. These interviews also covered a range of themes in an open way including questions about their current post and specialty, pay and grading, staff appraisals, training opportunities, childcare and flexible working arrangements and relations with colleagues and patients.

The informal interviews with management and nursing staff normally lasted between 40 and 60 minutes. The interviews with both management and nursing staff were carried out over a 15-month period between November 1992 and January 1994. The bulk of the interviews were carried out by the authors. A smaller number of interviews were conducted by a field interviewer experienced in employment and ethnicity research.

Methods: The postal survey
In order to complement the qualitative data collected in the six case study areas described in the earlier chapter, the postal survey provided detailed information on the current distribution of ethnic minority nursing staff across grades and specialties and sought out the reasons for the current pattern.

Sampling of nurse employers
The selection of the nurse employers for inclusion in the postal survey proved to be very complex as a result of a number of issues beyond the control of the study, including the reorganisation presently under way within the NHS, in particular the move towards trust status. However, at the time of the survey, it was found that there was a total of 458 nurse employers and FHSAs in England comprising 368 district health authorities and trusts and 90 FHSAs. These nurse employers were stratified by type of employer (for example, DHA, trust, FHSA) and then in descending order of ethnic minority concentration.

In the absence of data relating to the ethnic minority nursing concentration within DHA or nurse employer boundaries, it was decided to take a proxy of ethnic minority concentration in local authority boundaries in which the nurse employers predominantly fell. It was found that 66 nurse employers fell in local authority boundaries that had high ethnic minority concentration, 154 in areas with a medium ethnic minority concentration and 237 within low ethnic minority concentration areas. To ensure a reasonable chance of catching a significant number of ethnic minority nursing and midwifery staff, it was decided to oversample those nurse employers that fell in areas with high and medium concentrations of ethnic minority populations. A sampling fraction of 1 in 2 was chosen for the high concentration stratum, 1 in 3 for the medium stratum and 1 in 6 for the low stratum, producing a sample of 123 employers. This comprised a total of 33 nurse employers from areas of high ethnic minority concentration, 51 nurse employers from areas with a medium ethnic minority concentration and 39 nurse employers from areas with a low ethnic minority concentration.

The questionnaire and its administration

The development of the questionnaire followed a three stage procedure. In the first stage, a topic guide was developed. Informal group discussions were held with ethnic minority nurses from one London based nurse employer where the major issues of concern to them were identified. At the same time, a trawl of literature identified the main issues relating to nursing development generally.

In the second stage, the draft questionnaire was used in face-to-face pilot with nursing staff, and any remaining queries about question phrasing were ironed out. In the third stage a postal pilot survey in two trusts encompassing 500 nursing staff was undertaken to investigate if nursing staff had any problems in completing the questionnaire. The questionnaire was modified in the light of these pilots before being sent out to nursing and midwifery staff in the main survey. The response rate in the postal pilot survey was 71 per cent.

The final questionnaire asked ethnic minority and white nursing and midwifery staff detailed questions about their career histories including:

• how they got there;

• the training they undertook;

• how long it took them to get to their current position;

• their pattern of work;

• their grading;

• opportunities for training and further career development;

• levels of job satisfaction;

• questions about working relations with colleagues and patients including asking nursing and midwifery staff about their experience of racial discrimination and harassment.

A copy of the postal questionnaire is included in Appendix 2.

The postal survey comprised three stages. The first involved the questionnaire and a letter explaining the study being sent to the sample of nursing and midwifery staff. The second stage involved a reminder letter being sent out approximately three to four weeks after the first stage to those who had not already responded. A final reminder letter and an accompanying questionnaire were sent out in the final phase of the study, again approximately three to four weeks after the initial reminder letter was sent out to those who had not returned the initial questionnaire.

There are, of course, various positive and negative aspects to relying on questionnaire data in this way. The confidential nature of the survey hopefully enabled respondents to answer honestly without worrying about any consequences, which is crucially important for the types of sensitive issues that were examined. The most efficient way of tapping their feelings about their jobs and work conditions was to ask them directly, and we could not possibly have collected information from such a large sample using any other methodology. However, a proportion of the questions asked respondents to recall events or information retrospectively, which may introduce an element of bias as people will inevitably be somewhat selective in their personal memories. In addition, questionnaires of this nature cannot demonstrate a causal connection between the things that are asked about, but can indicate associations and correlates, and conclusions about process from cross-sectional data of the nature generated by this questionnaire need to be drawn tentatively.

Response rates

Before questionnaires were sent out, each selected employer was asked to submit a list of all of their nursing and midwifery staff together with their work addresses. Three quarters of the employers agreed to submit a complete list of their nurse employees. After a process of negotiation, a total of 93 employers agreed to participate in the survey comprising 27 nurse employers from areas with a high ethnic minority concentration, 37 nurse employers from areas with a medium ethnic minority concentration and 29 nurse employers from areas with a low ethnic minority concentration. Reflecting the changing face of the NHS, the greatest number of nurse employers participating were trusts. It should be noted that only 84 actually submitted lists of their nurse employees, the remaining nine only agreed to participate on condition that they could distribute the questionnaires to their nursing and midwifery staff themselves. Two of these then dropped out at the very last moment, leaving the total at 91 nurse employers.

Once the employers had been selected and had agreed to take part, the second stage in the sampling involved the selection of nursing and midwifery staff within these participating employers. The total number of permanent staff employed by the 91 employers participating in the study was just over 75,000. Using a sampling fraction of 1 in 3, a total of 23,251 nursing and midwifery staff were selected to participate in the postal survey. The survey was launched in the second week of February and closed at the end of April 1994. The response rate at the close of the study, after the final reminder letter and the accompanying questionnaire had been sent out and time allowed for return, was 62 per cent. The total number of completed questionnaires received was 14,330.

Sample weighting

Statistical weighting of cases allows different individuals to be given a different 'weight' in analysis. For example, weighting is used if the sample does not accurately reflect the actual population from which it is drawn. There might be too many men in a sample, for instance, in comparison to the numbers in the full population. In this case, in analyses, men might be given a lower 'weight' to make up for the fact that they are over-represented.

As was the case in the current postal survey, studies of ethnic minorities often over sample the important minority groups in order to ensure that there are enough people from those groups in the final responses. Once all the responses are in, the sample must then be weighted to correct for this sampling bias, to ensure that the proportions of ethnic minorities in the analyses are the same as in the full population.

Although details about the actual numbers of ethnic minority nursing and midwifery staff in the full population were difficult to establish, oversampling was achieved by taking more nursing and midwifery staff from nurse employers in locations where there were higher levels of ethnic minorities in the whole area. The description of the sampling above highlighted the fact that there were three layers of sampling. In areas of low ethnic populations, 1 in 6 of the nurse employers were taken. In areas of middle range ethnic populations, 1 in 3 of the nurse employers were taken. In areas of high ethnic populations, 1 in 2 of the nurse employers were taken. To correct for this bias, the following weights were assigned to these three layers. Nursing staff who came from employers in the first layer were given a weight of 1.5. Nursing staff in the second layer were given a weight of 0.75. Nursing staff in the third layer were given a weight of 0.5. It is usual to give weights with an average value of approximately 1, as this means that the final number of cases in the sample, the 'weighted sample', approximately matches the original number of cases. The average weight given in this case turned out to be 0.9, so final adjustments were made to bring this up to 1, leaving the total number of cases in the study as identical before and after weighting.

All subsequent analyses on the responses to the postal survey were subject to this weighting procedure.

PART II

PERSONNEL POLICY AND PRACTICE FOR NHS NURSES AND MIDWIVES IN SIX CASE STUDY EMPLOYERS

Overview and summary

This section presents the results from six qualitative case studies of NHS nurse and midwife employers, undertaken within six district authorities and trusts. A total of 156 interviews were conducted with nurses, midwives and managers from a range of levels, in order to study policies and practices within the NHS as they affected opportunities for staff. Six main areas were investigated with each of the case study employers:

- *Recruitment and selection.* Five of the six employers had written policies on recruitment, but in many areas implementation of the policies was not systematic and training in recruitment methods was not always given appropriate priority.

- *Staff appraisals.* Three of the six employers had introduced a formal system of appraisal. However, even within these areas, implementation was partial and it was rare to find nurses below the grade of ward manager who had been formally assessed. Many managers were expected to undertake appraisals without having received any training. Attitudes to formal appraisals amongst nursing staff were mixed.

- *Training and development.* Training was agreed by a process of informal negotiation followed by a procedure of application and approval involving senior managers. Theoretically, the allocation of training opportunities was based on the needs of the service and the particular development needs of the individual staff member. However, in practice, there was little systematic identification of training needs. Consequently, there was a general feeling amongst both white and ethnic minority staff that the allocation of training was not equitable. Also, fees and time off were not as easily available as they used to be.

- *Equal opportunities.* All six employers had a formal equal opportunities policy, but there was a widespread lack of clarity over enforcement. Monitoring information was sometimes collected for reference in individual cases, but was not analysed to provide an overall picture. None of the organisations studied had created an atmosphere in which the avoidance of racial discrimination was seen to be a priority. Staff perceptions of equal opportunities reflected the lack of clear practice.

- *Flexible working arrangements.* Despite written policies, flexible working and child-care provisions by the employers did not reflect the needs of the nursing staff. Workplace nurseries operated within 'office hours' which did not suit nurses on shift work; prices were beyond the reach of most nursing staff.

- *Relations with colleagues and patients.* Nurses from ethnic minority groups reported extensive experience of racial harassment in their work sometimes from colleagues, often from patients. Few had reported these problems to the authorities. Most felt that they were forced to accept racial harassment as 'part of the job'.

3 Recruitment and selection procedures

Access to employment opportunities is a key factor in determining lives and lifestyles. Job opportunities, generally, are determined by the way in which the labour market operates. For black people, however, equal access to such opportunities is the function of the ability and willingness of employers to operate personnel systems that do not discriminate on racial grounds and actively promote equality of opportunity. If personnel systems are to deliver equal job opportunities, employers need to respond positively to the legal provisions of the Race Relations Act 1976 and the recommendations of the Commission's Code of Practice in employment, which received parliamentary approval in 1984 (Commission for Racial Equality 1989: 7).

As this quotation from the CRE suggests, equal opportunities begin at selection for recruitment. If done properly rates of turnover should be reduced and staff encouraged to develop fully their skills. Service standards and recruitment policy are intimately linked. Ensuring that the best candidate for the job is recruited is essential in attaining high standards of service. However, assumptions and stereotypes about ethnic minority groups can affect selection decisions and a recruitment system that disadvantages any particular group is a waste of talent and skills. All staff involved in the selection and recruitment of staff need to be given clear information on how to dispense their responsibilities fairly. It is likely that a policy statement alone will not be enough.

However, the first step in implementing a fair and open recruitment process will often begin with the drawing up of detailed guidelines, sometimes in the form of a code of practice. Translating equal opportunities in recruitment from paper into daily practice is only possible when all staff involved in recruitment and selection process are made aware of good practice. In fact, a code of practice covering the recruitment and selection of staff is part of the formula used by the CRE to measure employers' commitment to equal opportunities. Clearly outlining procedures in a code of practice may go some of the way to eliminate the scope for discrimination in recruitment, and will seek to ensure that recruitment and selection are based on non-discriminatory work related criteria.

Policy documents including codes of practice are the 'public face' of an employer. They represent the 'official' managerial approach to employment practice. These written records are the way employers can 'be seen to be fair' to both employees and the wider community. An equal opportunities employer must be committed to unprejudiced competition for posts. To address this issue the NHS Management Executive has set up a programme of action to promote equality of opportunity for ethnic minority staff in the NHS. One of the key goals concerns recruitment and selection procedures:

> All staff involved in advertising, sifting and short-listing job applications and selecting candidates, [to] have received training in fair recruitment and selection procedures (including training on race and sex discrimination) by a specified target date (NHS Management Executive 1993: 7).

NHS employers are expected to train and update all staff involved with the recruitment process. The programme of action thus acknowledges that selecting the right person for the job is crucial in developing an effective workforce.

This section is based upon the findings in six case study areas. In particular we have examined issues which directly affect the career opportunities of ethnic minority nurses, midwives, health visitors and unqualified staff. We have concentrated upon the routes of attracting suitable candidates, including internal and external methods. The selection process was explored, including short-listing for interview and the selection interview itself. Within these broad categories we examined the extent of formal (written recruitment policy) and informal (unwritten but commonly accepted) recruitment practices. We examined the extent to which internal labour markets were utilised and the implications this might have for ethnic minority staff. We looked at the roles played by the personnel department and nursing management in the decision-making process, leading up to and including appointment.

One of our six case study employers did not provide us with their written policies on recruitment. This employer had just become a Trust and was undergoing great change. It was spread over a number of sites, each offering a distinct clinical specialty. Each clinical directorate within the Trust had its own recruitment process. One of the Trust's first and largest tasks was in trying to rationalise the recruitment procedure Trust-wide. This had started in earnest with the review of current recruitment policies and the setting of standards of good practice. At the time it did not have a comprehensive Trust-wide policy on recruitment and felt it inappropriate to give us access to policy documents undergoing revision. One of the five remaining employers did not have a specific recruitment policy. However, brief mention was made of the recruitment procedure in their equal opportunities policy.

Recruitment policy for all five of the employers began with their commitment to equal opportunities. Job applicants would not be discriminated against on the basis of ethnic origin, sex, sexual orientation, marital status, age, disability or trade union activity. Some employers included 'race', colour, nationality, creed and social background and one included HIV and like diseases.

Job advertisements

Advertising vacancies

The first stage of any recruitment process is the mechanism of attracting suitable candidates. This was always done by advertising the vacancy. The purpose of advertising a job vacancy is to bring it to the attention of the appropriate audience and to produce an adequate number of suitable applicants. The decision to circulate job information, the format this will take and how and where to advertise will determine the level and type of applicants to any particular post.

The primary responsibility for preparing advertisements in all six of our case study areas was that of the nursing management, as they were 'aware of the essential characteristics of the vacancy and the type of person they are looking for to fill it'.

The function of the personnel department was largely in giving technical support or coordinating the advertising process. Their role was to ensure that the text of advertisements did not breach discrimination laws and was generally in line with employers' equal opportunities policies. In particular, they ensured that only job-related criteria were used and that the equal opportunities statement appeared in all job advertisements. Positive action initiatives were highlighted by the personnel department where possible by encouraging under-represented groups to apply for vacancies.

Reasons for advertising internally

Advertising vacancies internally utilises internal labour markets and means that employees are protected from competition from the external labour market. Entry level posts within nurse employers are usually re-stricted to unqualified (A/B grades) or newly qualified (C/D grades) posts. These constitute two distinct types of internal labour market as described by Althauser and Kalleberg (1981). Unqualified staff operate within a 'firm' internal labour market which offers secure employment but few or no career opportunities. Qualified staff operate within a much wider occupational labour market. Their specialised skills and knowledge are essential in carrying out the functions of the post, and they are offered employment with potential promotions and career opportunities.

The majority of our six case study employers used a combination of internal only or internal and simultaneous external advertisements. This decision was dependent upon the grade and specialty of the post. One employer advertised internally and externally simultaneously for all posts. Another would advertise internally and externally simultaneously, but this would be grade dependent. The higher the grade the more likely it was to be simultaneously advertised.

A minority of employers advertised internally amongst their own workforce, prior to any external advertisement. If posts were not filled in this manner only then would they go on to external advertisements. The decision to advertise internally first, before any external advertisement, was usually triggered by three main factors. These included the closure of hospitals, departments, wards or beds in the reorganisation of health services; the existence of a school of nursing; or a line manager's or the personnel department's perceived knowledge of the internal labour market.

It is argued that the reorganisation of the health service with movement away from hospital to primary care in the community has led to a loss of hospital-based jobs. In places where this was the case, employees under threat of redundancy within each employer were informed of vacancies first. If not filled by staff at risk of redundancy, vacancies would appear in an internal bulletin. This was known as the staff vacancy bulletin. Only if vacancies were not filled internally would the advertisement be placed externally. As a personnel department representative in mental health said:

> We're going through an expansion of services in the community and a contraction of hospital services. Because we are having to re-deploy services a lot of our recruitment is taking place internally, the first opportunities will go to people whose jobs will disappear as a result of the reorganisation.

These were not the only internal candidates who would be given 'first choice'. Managers complained that their own nursing students were unable to get jobs when advertisements went external. They often found themselves competing with candidates with higher qualifications and more experience. In the light of these experiences many entry level posts, usually at grade D, were only advertised within their own school of nursing. We found that two of our case study employers would only advertise D grade posts solely in the school of nursing. We found this to be particularly the case within midwifery. As a director of midwifery services explained, 'I have a policy which seeks to ensure that my [midwifery] graduates have the opportunity to apply for a fixed-term contract'.

In these cases, the vacancies would not even go into the internal staff vacancy bulletin unless suitable candidates could not be found amongst the newly qualified nurses or midwives. This practice was not unique to midwifery: this senior nurse in care of the elderly suggested a similar rationale, 'if it is a D grade [post] we like to employ our own girls from the nursing school, so we will only advertise in the school'. One employer made it quite clear that external advertising was 'the last resort' and should always be preceded by consideration of internal recruitment.

Internal recruitment was not always restricted solely to entry level posts. One employer linked recruitment at all levels to staff development. Advertising internally ensured that some level of internal mobility took place. At least one senior nurse felt this was essential to staff morale. However, selecting solely from internal candidates did not always ensure the best candidates were appointed. A senior nurse in midwifery explained the procedure:

> ... if we know there are quite a few people ready for promotion, why go outside? Let's face it, we know these girls. Usually, we advertise internally. If we cannot find anyone to step into the post after interview, it may be an idea to re-interview them. Maybe they did not interview well.

The decision to advertise internally and use vacancies to promote from within or to go external and open the post up to candidates from outside was often triggered by nurse managers, perceived knowledge of their staff. A director of nursing services for mental health stated that 'if we are aware that there are people on the staff who are ready to be promoted to that grade, in such cases we don't need to look outside'. Or as this midwifery services manager put it, 'if I think I have not got the right calibre of staff inside I will offer it externally. I have got enough of the right calibre of staff to do that. I don't need to advertise externally'.

However, using internal recruitment for promotional purposes overall was rare. Only one of our case study employers did this on a regular basis. The head of midwifery services for this area explained her approach, 'every four to six months I try to do some E-F up-grades. F grade posts are used to try and give a career structure to E grade midwives'. This nurse manager would confine advertisements to the clinical directorate to ensure that only those within the departments could possibly apply. Promotion will be examined in more detail in the next section.

Jenkins (1986) points out the possible negative effect of internal recruitment on black workers. If black workers are overwhelmingly in low grade jobs they are less likely to benefit from internal vacancies as they are less likely to be seen as promotional material. In particular some occupational groups simply do not have a promotional ladder. Jenkins gives the example of nursing auxiliaries, for whom the situation has changed little in recent reorganisations. Auxiliaries have moved from having virtually no career ladder to an extremely limited one within two grades.

Internal recruitment could be fraught with difficulties. Information was not always internally circulated as fully as expected. Managers given responsibility for updating staff at ward or unit meetings were rarely, if ever evaluated as this personnel manager for community services stated:

> We have had some concerns from people that they haven't received the [internal] bulletin. It's generally sent to the nurse manager ... We assume they are putting it on the public notice-board.

Notice-boards were sometimes tucked away off the main corridors or reception areas. Staff would need to be diligent to ensure notice boards were checked on a regular basis. However, some members of management recognised that even strategically placed notice-boards were often overlooked and ignored.

A contraction of nursing posts has led to employers becoming more likely to advertise internally, first. This is used as a way of ensuring not only that their own nursing students get in, but that their own staff have an opportunity to get on. As we have seen, internal advertisements can boost morale as the employers is seen to be 'looking after its own' with first refusals. However, in the long term, internal recruitment can lead to stagnation and cut off the supply of new ideas and approaches. Internal recruitment is also likely to perpetuate the status quo and inequalities which are likely to act to the disadvantage of minority groups.

Promotion
Many interviewees stated that opportunities to be 'made-up' or promoted after attaining the relevant skills necessary for the next grade were extremely limited. Promotion was widely perceived by nursing staff and managers as virtually non-existent. Applying for a post at a higher grade and going through the standard recruitment process was the only way to move up the career ladder. Posts could only be applied for when vacancies occurred. Even when vacancies arose there was no guarantee the

post would be kept as budget savings were constantly being examined. As one senior community manager said 'when someone is in a job they are there to stay and when they move on the post might not be kept. They might need to save two per cent on the budget and axe the post'.

Contraction of the occupational market has put a break on the mobile nature of the profession. Qualified nursing staff felt it had become difficult for them to gain a wide range of experience by moving from post to post. Equal opportunities policies were often blamed for the declining opportunities for promotion. As one personnel department representative explained, 'partly because of our equal opportunities policy there is no longer any career progression. Because of equal opportunities it is considered that anyone who wants to apply for a post should do so ... all vacancies are advertised'.

Regrading for former enrolled nurses after the completion of a conversion course was one of the few promotional occasions. But, becoming an RGN did not always generate a promotion as this personnel department representative explained:

> A number of nurses are graded D and they have gone on the conversion and converted to the RGN. They are not going to get an upgrading on the basis of that but they are going to get a new job description and have some new duties.

On rare occasions we did find that other sorts of promotion took place. Not all posts were open to competition, as one personnel department representative explained to us:

> What sometimes happens is if someone has the relevant experience they might be appointed in an E grade post at a D grade salary for six months or something. After six months because they have been doing the duties of an E grade there is an agreement they will be promoted. It's a way of getting them on the ward and keeping them there really. I don't think it is strictly allowed but it does go on.

However, this practice was not widespread. We came across a single example amongst our six employers. Nonetheless, managers unable to reward staff with promotion would use other methods. As this community manager explained, 'I reward with time off. It's an acknowledgement of the effort they have put in. After [completing post-basic] ENB training we can't pay more money or promote, and staff know that, but good work gets an extra couple of days off'.

Training opportunities could also be used as rewards. This personnel department representative suggested that 'the areas in which they [nurse managers] can reward are training. There is a limited training budget. I would have thought that the more able staff would be given a greater opportunity for training than less able staff'. Similarly, increasing responsibility was also used as a reward for staff. A senior nurse in care of the elderly explained how this worked. 'We have started self-medication, opened carers groups, we allow them to go on study days. We allow them to take charge of their unit to help them along.'

Many line managers across our six case study areas clearly felt constrained by the lack of promotional opportunities for their staff. It was widely felt that there were no longer any formal mechanisms in place to reward or retain staff. On occasions we found this had led to the development of a system of informal rewards. We came across time off, training opportunities and extra responsibility, all of which were used to reward staff. Criteria for rewards were unwritten and haphazard. The decision to reward was the nurse managers alone, these were private agreements between managers and their staff.

We would argue that the idiosyncratic nature of such rewards left them open to abuse. These informal procedures were not recorded or monitored ensuring no opportunity for those not rewarded to register their dissatisfaction. These reward systems are often unique to individual line managers and largely unknown to more senior and personnel department management. On rare occasions we did find that senior and/or personnel department management had knowledge of the operation of such systems. We found they were reluctant to intervene even when it was acknowledged that such activities contravened employers' written policies.

Methods of external advertisement
There were broadly three different types of external recruitment channels. These were divided into local and national channels:

- Advertisement and the circulation of vacant posts in the local area. This often included job centres, community groups and the local press;

- The London Implementation Group (LIG) which would send vacancies to nursing staff in the Greater London area who were at threat of redundancy;

- National advertisements in professional nursing and managerial journals such as the Nursing Times, Nursing Standard and the Health Service Journal.

In London the internal circulation of vacancy information would be followed by informing the London Implementation Group (LIG) before an external advertisement was placed. The London Implementation

Group (LIG) was formed as a result of the recommendations of the Tomlinson report. LIG were informed of all vacancies in the London area. They circulated details to staff who had been 'displaced' or who were about to become redundant in Greater London.

When vacancies went external a standard pattern was usually identifiable. Qualified posts (C to I) tended to be advertised nationally in the professional journals, most notably the Nursing Times. Some senior posts of G and above might go into the Health Service Journal instead. Unqualified posts for auxiliaries and health care assistants tended to be advertised in the local press.

Reasons for advertising externally

Most employers divided up external advertising strategies between local and national channels. As already indicated, choosing between the local and national channels would often be dependent upon the grade of the post to be advertised. Two employers had a written policy of only using local advertisements for unqualified staff. The local press was clearly identified as being 'suitable for ancillary vacancies'. Posts requiring professional qualifications would not be expected to appear in the local press. These would go to national advertisement. Another two employers operated this policy in practice although it differed from their written policy.

Labour market conditions and equal opportunities were key reasons for nurse and senior managers 'going local' when looking for unqualified staff. The following responses were typical of the answers provided by managers responsible for recruitment:

> For a lot of our jobs at the moment we would advertise just locally because there is quite a good pool (the Director of the personnel department).

> It's equal opportunities to trawl locally (a neighbourhood manager).

> We would advertise locally [for auxiliaries] mainly in the local newspapers because we want to pitch the advert at local people (a ward manager working in the mental health directorate).

It was suggested that advertising locally would encourage candidates for auxiliary posts who would be representative of the local ethnic communities. A senior nurse working in general medicine stated that they advertised in the 'most widely read local paper to ensure we got the proper ethnic mix'.

The same rationale was not used for qualified staff. The local community was usually not considered to contain a pool of qualified personnel. The higher the grade of post the more likely it was to be advertised nationally, as this director of community services pointed out. 'If we want people with quite a lot of skills, like community nurses, they have to be advertised outside. With auxiliaries we might just advertise within the Trust area'.

On rare occasions vacancies for qualified staff would be advertised locally. This would be for specific, specialist posts. Local advertisements for specialist posts would sometimes coincide with a simultaneous national advert. This personnel department representative outlined the standard procedure: 'The classic case would go straight to the Nursing Times, or Evening Standard. Any qualified nurse [post] is likely to be advertised in the Nursing Times, but we would also try the local press for certain posts.'

Much was made of the cost of external advertisements and senior nurse managers perceived it as an expensive way to attract suitable candidates. One departmental head suggested that financial restrictions meant that they could not always afford to advertise externally even when this was considered the most effective option. Because of the cost implications, managers responsible for placing advertisements were generally reluctant to try new avenues. Sticking to tried and tested sources of advertising was popular.

One employer 'encouraged' the use of a range of papers in which to advertise vacancies. The extent to which this was done was unknown. Two employers suggested that they used the ethnic minority press in addition to other local or national channels. We were given an example of a post for a 'thalassaemia nurse' which was advertised in the ethnic minority press. However, according to a manager in the personnel department, the ethnic minority press was not an effective channel in attracting professional nursing staff because 'if you are a nurse you are probably going to look in the Nursing Times and not the Voice'.

The government run job centre was used for unqualified staff in five of our six case study employers. It was not perceived by nurse or senior managers or the personnel department as an effective channel in attracting qualified nursing staff. Jenkins (1986) points out the poor status of the job centre amongst other employers. Our findings were similar on this matter. Managers had little faith in finding skilled or qualified staff through the job centre. It was widely felt that qualified staff would look to the professional journals when seeking a new post and would not go to a job centre.

Overall, employers preferred to try and fill vacancies internally. If this strategy was found to be unsuccessful only then would an external advertisement be considered.

Informal methods of recruitment

Word of mouth was used as a way of finding suitable candidates but recruitment would never be restricted solely to informal channels. Word of mouth was simply a way of spreading information regarding vacancies over the widest area. As a director of nursing services for mental health explained, 'staff talk to relatives, friends, neighbours telling them that a job is going'.

Unsolicited curriculum vitaes and letters of application were usually passed to the appropriate line managers. They were normally retained on file for several months in case a suitable vacancy arose. If such a vacancy arose, the CVs and letters of application would be forwarded to the personnel department by the line managers. These applicants would then enter the standard recruitment process. A slight problem arose in that there was no way of ensuring that a level of screening had not already taken place. This was explained by a senior personnel manager responsible for the care of the elderly directorate:

> Some managers have a lot of CVs going directly to them, so they keep them and probably reply to them themselves or let us have them when there is a vacancy so we can send out details. We have no way of knowing if managers are sending us all the CVs for further details to be sent out or not.

Informal word of mouth was never used as the sole method of attracting candidates; although informal networks were utilised in communicating information regarding vacancies.

Job descriptions

Written policy on job descriptions and person specifications

All five case study employers with written guidelines on recruitment practices expected that all posts would have a job description and person specification. In some cases, these would be drawn up by the appropriate nurse manager. However, within other employers the job description and person specification were to be drawn up jointly in conjunction with representatives from the personnel department. The person specification was used to distinguish between essential and desirable job-related selection criteria. In a minority of employers a personnel department representative compiled a checklist of which essential and desirable selection criteria each applicant satisfied. Two employers suggested that approval to recruit would not be given unless a job description and person specification were drawn up prior to advertising. Only one employer suggested that the person in post should be consulted about their job description when a vacancy arose.

Job descriptions and person specifications in practice

We found that five of the six employers had written job descriptions and person specifications for every post, although the range of staff most often involved in their development varied. This was usually dependent upon the organisational structure and the grade of the vacancy. The higher the grade of the post the more senior the staff involved in devising the job description and person specification. Job descriptions and person specifications for unqualified staff were sometimes used as a training ground for senior staff nurses to practise their skills. Three employers suggested that the person in post would be routinely consulted on changes to their job description.

The personnel department's input into job descriptions and person specifications was limited, often being restricted to the structure and not the content of job descriptions. As a general rule the personnel department would not usually be involved and would only participate if requested. The personnel department mostly saw their role as an advisory one with responsibility for job descriptions clearly in the hands of nurse managers.

Short-listing and interviewing

Written policy on short-listing and interviewing procedure

Written policies amongst our case study employers made it clear that the role of the nurse manager is to initiate the recruitment process and follow it through to the offer of an appointment. The personnel department exists to advise managers and to take care of the routine administration.

Only one employer suggests that the personnel department should be present at all interviews, whenever possible. This employer suggests a much more strategic role for the personnel department in organising the interview panel and having input into the decision-making process. In this case, it was the responsibility of the personnel department representative to ensure the interview panel agreed the order and range of questions prior to interviewing the first candidate and to ensure that all questions related to the requirements of the job. It was generally agreed that the interview panel meet prior to the interview to agree the person specification and how the interview was to be conducted. Only one employer had written guidelines on the role of external assessors which would ensure they were briefed in the recruitment process prior to interview. This same employer was explicit that short-listing and interviewing must be done by more than one person, at least one of whom must be aware of the employer's equal opportunities policy. This was also the only employer who dealt with the recruitment procedure for staff requiring work permits. In order to offer the post to someone requiring a work permit the employer must be able to show that it has been advertised nationally within the United Kingdom and internationally, European Union-wide. All employers recommended that staff who take part in the short-listing also take part in the interviews and vice versa.

Five out of six employers did not mention the status of informal visits by candidates for posts prior to interview in their written policies.

Short-listing and interviewing in practice

The tasks of short-listing and interviewing, although grade dependent, were clearly felt to be the responsibility of the nurse management and were jealously guarded, as this ward manager explained. 'If I'm going to be interviewing with other people I will let them see the application forms, but I have the final decision.'

In contrast to the written policy not all those involved in the short-listing were consistently involved in the interviewing. It was not uncommon for half the interview panel not to have been involved in the initial short-listing.

The vast majority of candidates were selected on the basis of the job description and/or the person specification. These answers were typical of those we were given:

> All jobs have a job description and a person specification. We have a procedure that the personnel department will not accept a post for advertisement unless it has a job description and a person specification attached (a personnel manager).

> At the end of the day we score them against the specification (the Director of mental health unit).

> We try to evaluate a person by how they meet the essential and desirable qualities outlined (a ward manager working in the mental health unit).

In one extreme case, we came across a nurse manager who did not use written job descriptions or person specifications in short-listing candidates or in the criteria used for interviews. In this case not only was there no person specification, there were no written criteria on which candidates were selected at all. This ward manager who was solely responsible for the short-listing decided what was important by 'keeping it in mind. I don't have a written person specification, I just have it in my own mind'.

In this case, interviewers had no written criteria on which to evaluate candidates. Again this ward manager would decide what was important and 'keep it in mind.' The personnel department were aware of this situation and that written criteria in the selection process were not used. Personnel department representatives were sometimes invited to interviews but regardless of the ad hoc procedure the final decision of who to recruit would be the ward manager's.

We found that formalising procedures did not always ensure fairness or consistency; as this personnel department representative for general medicine pointed out. 'Sometimes a person specification is used, but it's not something that is used very formally in the hospital at the moment.' Similarly, interview questions were usually decided on before the interview, but this did not mean they were always adhered to, as this director of nursing services for mental health explained:

> There will be a standard form to which you short-list them against ... which looks at the skills you would need to be a staff grade nurse, what type of experience we expect an E grade nurse to have. This is drawn up prior to the interview. I wouldn't like to say we stick tenaciously to it because individuals are individuals and the things you may wish to pursue with one individual you might not with another.

In this particular case it was not just the candidate's qualifications, experience and performance in the interview that candidates were judged on: as she said, 'we take into consideration the application form, their approach to the interview, whether they've been to talk to us, what interests they have shown in the place, how feasible it was for them to come and visit us'.

Despite their lack of mention in written policies, it was often the case that the informal visit had become a part of the selection process. Pre-interview visits were not the only unwritten specification that candidates would be judged on. Candidates who were not British nationals would also be severely disadvantaged as this senior nurse in care of the elderly explained:

> It is hard not to be discriminatory. For example, when you need someone urgently and they need a work permit, this will take some time. A recent example occurred when we selected someone who needed a work permit. We could not get one [a work permit] because the job was only advertised internally. So if the post is advertised internally there is no point even selecting those people [who need a work permit] to attend for interviews.

Documentation from a central personnel department sometimes weighted criteria in a way that was seen as inappropriate, as this senior community nurse manager outlined:

> I do not like the ones [forms] we get from personnel as all criteria are given equal weight. Appearance is given equal weight with communication skills. We had another scale that we ticked that asked about [the candidates's] interest

in trade unions, family circumstances; we did not ask this but it was still on the form. Now we concentrate on the way candidates answer questions.

Written criteria and rigorous scoring were not always equated with fairness. The candidate with the highest score was not always the person selected for the post. There was sometimes a 'bit of fixing' to ensure that the favourite candidate scored higher than all the other candidates. It was reported that this was done to cover those involved in interviewing, as the score sheets were returned to the personnel department and the panel could have been asked to account for its decision in not offering the post to the best candidate for the job.

Following the pattern found for advertising and job descriptions, the personnel department's involvement in short-listing and interviewing was usually dependent upon the grade of the post and whether it was an internal or external appointment. An internal qualified appointment was likely to involve the personnel department. However, this would rarely be for posts below grade E and was often for grades G and above. Employers with schools of nursing would often invite a personnel department representative onto the interview panel when entry level posts had only been advertised in the school. Certain specialties, in particular mental health and midwifery, tended to invite external panel members on a more regular basis. It was suggested to us this was because these specialties were more likely to attract internal candidates already based in these specialties. With a personnel department representative on the interview panel these appointments were more likely to be seen to be fair.

Short-listing and interviewing of unqualified staff would often be undertaken by ward managers alone or in conjunction with senior staff nurses (grades E-F). As with the writing of job descriptions and person specifications these grades of posts would be used as a training ground for more junior qualified staff.

One community nurse manager suggested that *all* grades of staff would be formally involved in the short-listing procedure. Although, this would be dependent upon grade for instance, an A grade took part in the short-listing for another A grade post. She explained 'If you are involved you can't moan if the person does not shape up, but also you feel motivated because you feel people are interested in your views. However, this would not be followed through to the interview stage. Only qualified staff would be involved in the actual interview.

The majority of managers suggested they used a structured interview format in which all questions were based on the person specification or job description. However, candidates were not asked the same or even standardised questions. Answers given about scoring were often vague and it seems unlikely that any systematic scoring procedure was used on a regular basis. However, as we did not sit in or observe any interviews we can say little about the actual validity and reliability of judgements about interview candidates (for a full discussion of this issue see Smith and Robertson 1993, chapter 10).

Unlike Jenkins' (1986) study of employment practice in the health service we found that both the personnel department and line managers were involved with the recruitment of staff. Nonetheless, decisions were overwhelmingly the responsibility of the nurse management. Equal weighting of interviewers' ratings rarely, if ever occurred, as it was widely accepted that the opinions of nurse managers carried more weight. Consequently, there exists a danger that inconsistencies in selection interview judgements may occur.

We did not find that the formalisation of recruitment and selection procedures was always equated with 'fairness'. Indeed, bias was sometimes justified on the grounds of time and money. In order to appease the people who run the health service bureaucracy, it was reported that there was a risk of paperwork being falsified. However, it is unlikely that line managers could be held accountable as only one personnel department out of the six employers had ever attempted to analyse recruitment data. It was collected 'in case there was a problem'. In the event of no problem occurring it was simply filed away before being destroyed. This view was legitimised by at least one employer whose policy documents clearly stated that recruitment documentation would only be needed in the accusation of discrimination. It made no mention of this information being routinely analysed.

Training for participation in recruitment

Written policy on training for staff involved in recruitment and selection

Only one of our case study employers laid strict guidelines for the training of those involved in the recruitment process. At least one person on the interview panel must have completed appropriate in-house training or a refresher course prior to interviewing. Uptake of such training would be closely monitored and the credibility of those appearing on interview panels would be checked on every occasion. A clear target was set, beyond which staff who had not undergone such training would be ineligible to participate in any stage of the recruitment process. Another four case study employers stated that all staff who take part in interview panels or any part of the recruitment process should have appropriate training, although none of these suggested how this would be implemented or how it would be monitored.

Training for staff involved in recruitment and selection in practice

In practice not a single employer could guarantee that at least one person on an interview panel had undergone any recruitment training. None of our case study employers could even estimate what proportion of their managers who were routinely involved in recruiting staff had undergone any training, as this director of general medical services explained:

> I think there is a need to go on training courses. We do have some training here, but we lack an overall strategy. What we have are flyers going out from the training department publicising a course on interviewing skills and a few people will go on it, but it's hit and miss and we could have a much better approach to it.

At least one ward manager did not feel confident in her ability to recruit and would welcome the opportunity to receive training. A more senior nurse manager in care of the elderly questioned the skills and abilities of those involved in the recruitment process:

> I have been on a two day course in interviewing. My technique and experience has developed over time, that's it. When I first started I had no training or experience so I was put in as an observer on interviews with another senior nurse. It was not until I had been on the course that I realised that a lot of the things she was doing you are not allowed to do.

Five employers stated that all staff involved in the recruitment procedure would have undergone some training but in practice this was not found to be the case. Only a small minority of staff involved in the selection and interviewing procedure had undergone training of any kind. This was usually in-house. It ranged from informal instruction from a more experienced and senior manager to workshops and study days lasting a couple of hours to two or three days. This example from a personnel department representative for community services was typical of the level of training given:

> ... we had someone in this morning who hadn't done recruitment and there was no opportunity for her to go on a half-day briefing, so basically I just talked through the process with her, which in itself is a form of training.

Training was rarely, if ever, updated and attending a study day once in the last two decades was considered adequate. Experience and actual 'hands on' practice was often used as a way of learning the 'right' way to recruit, as this ward manager in general medicine stated, 'it's been very much learning by practice'. Learning by practice would 'qualify' managers to carry out recruitment, as this director of mental health nursing services said, 'the fact they have sat in so many, so they are well-trained'.

Untrained managers and other staff involved in the recruitment process were often reliant upon booklets or recruitment packs. These contained all the relevant paper work and would sometimes have instructions on drawing up person specifications and how to short-list and conduct interviews.

Three of our case study employers were aware that a training problem existed and they were actively developing programmes to rectify this situation. A personnel representative for mental health services explained:

> We are trying to ensure that people who are responsible for short-listing and interviewing receive the appropriate training. The unit is developing a training programme to ensure that all managers have the necessary training before they undertake such tasks.

However, it was sometimes difficult to get all managers to attend training, as a personnel representative for community services explained:

> Our ideal would be that managers would have a regular training programme. If they hadn't had recruitment training for two years they come for a refresher, but we know that is not going to happen. What tends to happen is that those managers we consider to be pretty able recruiters will always be keen to update their skills and attend the briefings whereas the ones we really want to come on the training are the ones that are no damn good at it. We have identified a need. The next problem is getting managers to recognise the need.

Another employer was trying to involve the personnel department more in the recruitment process as a way of overcoming the lack of training for managers.

Summary and conclusion

There are a number of ways in which the recruitment and selection practices described in this chapter could impact on the experiences of ethnic minority staff and applicants. The NHS Management Executive (1993) lays down in its programme of action for ethnic minority staff the need to use the ethnic minority media to promote a culturally diverse image of the employer and to encourage ethnic minority applicants to posts in areas in which they are currently under-represented. However, the study found that the use of such media in advertising vacancies was limited and of little help. Indeed the use of such media was only utilised when vacancies arose which would involve the person caring for people with illnesses that were known disproportionately to affect ethnic minority groups, for example, certain haemaglobinapathies.

In common with other studies on recruitment practice, we found that utilising internal labour markets when vacancies occurred was a popular choice (see Jenkins 1986). However, internal labour markets were utilised formally, that is, vacancies were advertised internally and open to the normal competitive recruitment process, but this was restricted to internal candidates. Utilising internal labour markets was preferred on the basis of cost, time and flexibility. Money could be saved on advertising, selection could be rapid as candidates could be shortlisted on the basis of application forms and either formal or informal internal job appraisals, and managers were given a degree of flexibility to move staff to areas of increased demand from areas of decreased demand. It could also improve morale as employers are seen to be 'looking after their own' first.

Non-formalisation of selection criteria was rare, but, informal criteria can be hidden beneath formal procedures. However, where this occurred it is possible that informal selection criteria may play a role in reproducing the relative disadvantage of ethnic minority nursing staff. The exact relationship between formal and informal selection criteria and the actual decision making process is unknown as we did not observe, nor sit in on any selection interviews. We did not directly examine discrepancies between accounts given by managers involved in recruitment and selection and the formal written policies of their employers.

The collection and analysis of ethnic monitoring information on short-listed candidates requires immediate attention. Of particular urgency was the lack of training or updating in recruitment practice for nurse managers. The NHS Training Directorate (1992) sets out clear advice for the training needs of those involved in recruitment and selection:

> Do not underestimate the damaging effect of poor practice. If procedures are to be fair and effective, then managers need the support of specific guidelines and of training. Ensure that all appointment panels include at least one member trained in equal opportunities.

The Commission for Racial Equality's (1994) code of practice for the elimination of racial discrimination in employment goes further and makes clear recommendations for the training of staff who are involved in recruitment and selection:

> Staff responsible for short-listing, interviewing and selecting candidates should be ... given guidance or training on the effects which generalised assumptions and prejudices about race can have on selection decisions ... [and

be] made aware of the possible misunderstandings which can occur between persons of different cultural backgrounds (CRE 1994: 16).

We did not find that employers prioritised equal opportunities or race related training as it affected recruitment and selection. We found little evidence of employers' commitment to recommendations as outlined in the Commission for Racial Equality's Code of Practice for the elimination of racial discrimination and the promotion of equality of opportunity in employment (1994), or to the NHS Management Executive's publication, 'Ethnic minority staff in the NHS: a programme of action' (1993).

Although procedures may be formalised, it is difficult to know how these are enforced in practice if little or no training is given. Regardless of training, formalisation of procedures does not guarantee fairness. As we have seen, it is frequently possible to 'pre-determine the outcome', in particular when the personnel department is only peripherally involved. The personnel department staff should be recruitment experts and are responsible for employers' employment practice, good or otherwise. Their limited involvement in the selection procedure may be detrimental to the recruitment opportunities for ethnic minority workers. However, as we did not follow through the recruitment process for any single post we are unable to state whether or not this is likely to be the case. This chapter has shown that 'getting in' is key. In the following chapters we will explore how ethnic minority staff get on.

4 The assessment of nursing staff

This chapter examines how the work of qualified and unqualified nursing staff is assessed in six nurse employers. In particular, it seeks to investigate to what extent a formal performance management system in the form of the individual performance review (IPR) has been introduced for nursing staff working in the NHS, or whether more informal systems of assessment remain in operation. The chapter also goes on to examine the difficulties associated with introducing the individual performance review and the views of nursing staff on how they were currently assessed. A formal appraisal system is a major component of 'performance management' which has been defined as an 'inter-locking set of policies and practices which have as their focus the enhanced achievement of organisational objectives through a concentration on individual performance' (Storey and Sisson 1993: 132). It is held that the key elements of such a system are as follows:

• setting clear objectives for individual employees, derived normally from the organisation's strategy and a series of departmental purpose analyses (DPAs);

• formal monitoring and review of progress towards meeting these objectives;

• utilization of the outcomes of the review process to reinforce desired behaviour through differential rewards and/or to identify training and development needs.

These key elements of a performance management system are illustrated in Figure 4.1.

Townley (1991) has argued that there is an increasing tendency for management to adopt more systematic appraisal procedures. Data from several surveys seems to confirm this development. Long (1986) found that appraisal systems had been extended from managerial levels to include a greater number of blue-collar and secretarial staff. The proportion of first line supervisors being appraised rose from 60 per cent

Figure 4.1   Elements of a performance management system.

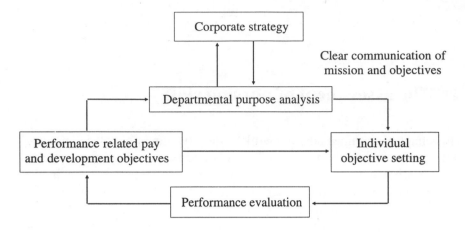

(taken from Storey and Sisson 1993: 133)

in 1977 to 78 per cent in 1985; whilst for clerical and secretarial staff it increased from 45 per cent to 66 per cent over the same time period. Similarly, for skilled and semi-skilled employees appraisals rose from 2 per cent in 1977 to 24 per cent in 1985. A study undertaken by the Institute of Personnel Management (IPM) (Bevan and Thompson 1992) undertook a sample survey looking at the prevalence of a performance management system within selected employers. Their survey had usable returns from 794 employers covering 4.3 million workers that is, nearly 20 per cent of the UK workforce. The survey found 20 per cent of the employing organisations reported that they had introduced a 'formal performance management programme'. However, their introduction had not led to their full implementation. When the IPM followed this survey up by undertaking a qualitative study involving visiting 26 organisations, they found that many of the organisations identified by the first study as practising formal performance management systems had little justification for making such a claim (Fletcher and Williams 1992).

Townley (1991) has contended that the explanation for this increasing introduction of formal performance management systems is 'in response to the problems of monitoring raised in the move away from the direct and technical supervision of work, to the greater degree of 'discretion', or 'flexibility', being devolved to the individual and/or work group'. Specifically, Storey and Sisson (1993) have identified four major factors that have led to such performance management systems being adopted. These are:

- increasing competition which has prompted companies to examine how their operations contribute to effectiveness or detract from it;

- governmental pressure on public sector organisations such as local government and the health service where accountability and measurement form a clear part of the political agenda;

- organisational restructuring which involves an emphasis upon the decentralisation of accountability to strategic business units and cost centres;

- the intent to redraw and redefine the boundaries of employee relations, in particular performance management systems offer a clear example of an attempt to individualise the employment relationship.

It is held that an effective review system should be individualised and conducted within a framework that considers an employee as capable of defining his or her own abilities for undertaking a post (Rowe 1992; Jones and Woodcock 1987). Rowe (1992: 288) goes on to state that:

> A system where ownership of and responsibility for the implementation of the criteria for the job are shifted to the employee is much more likely to succeed in developing the individual's potential, improving communication between staff, and motivating them to achieve their goals, and hence meet the organisation's overall aim.

However, there are some who argue that there are a number of potential disadvantages associated with performance management systems (ACAS 1988). It has been contended that they serve not as an 'objective' measure of individual performance but rather as a system of communicating managerial and organisational expectations and ethos to subordinates (Townley 1991). Townley's judgement that such systems essentially serve a 'control function' was based on findings which showed that self-assessment or self-rating was rarely used as a review tool. The reported lack of follow-up action, training and career development plans also questioned the sense of priority attached to appraisal as a 'two-way' communications system in most organisations.

Another criticism of performance management systems is their tendency to accentuate the focus on the productivity of the individual and the resultant reward of individual work and performance at the cost of obscuring the collective element of work. By failing to give sufficient weight to the team element of work, they can run the danger of increasing the stratification of workers and providing a narrow self-interest and individualism reflecting what Townley (1991) has referred to as 'the individualistic ethos' which she contends is the 'defining characteristic of [human resource management] HRM'.

Related to this concern about performance management systems and their emphasis on measurable targets for individuals is the increasing link made with performance related pay (PRP) (Storey 1992). There are two main types of individual PRP scheme: one involves the linking of pay to performances as measured by the achievement of specific individual objectives and the other – sometimes known as merit-rating – assesses performance in terms of certain behavioural traits such as problem-solving, reliability, initiative, and cooperation.

Advocates of PRP describe the purpose of its introduction as being 'to improve performance by converting the pay-bill from an indiscriminate machine to a more finely tuned mechanism, sensitive and responsive to a company's and employee's needs (Brading and Wright 1990).

However, critics of PRP contend that it fails adequately to take account of the collective nature of working in many areas of employment and therefore can 'undermine team spirit and cooperation'. As Storey and Sisson (1993: 141) argue 'employees may focus their attention on individual targets (especially if they are artificially contrived for the pay system) at the expense of the performance of the unit'. Similarly, Kline (1993) has identified other major problems when he states that the objective measurement of 'performance' would be difficult to make because the 'ratings will be influenced by personal prejudice, stereotypical attitudes to women and black workers and the value attached by the individual manager to the type of work done by the individual member of staff'.

The Individual Performance Review (IPR) in the NHS

The IPR in the NHS dates from the recommendations of the 1983 Griffiths Report. A personnel memorandum issued in September 1986 by the Department of Health and Social Security then made IPR obligatory for all general managers at regional and district level, and stated its intention to introduce it to all staff working in the NHS (NHS Training Directorate 1986).

However, its introduction to date has been slow, particularly amongst clinical nursing staff. A survey undertaken by the Institute of Health Services Management on behalf of the NHS Training Directorate (NHSTD) in 1991 found that 'IPR is still largely confined to the higher ranks of management and is still to find acceptance among clinically based staff' (IHSM 1991: 12).

The major argument put forward against the introduction of IPR for nursing staff has been that the clinical portion of their work does not lend itself to performance appraisal. On the other hand, advocates of the IPR argue that its introduction would allow nursing staff to highlight the scope of their work and therefore go some way towards achieving one of the aims of IPR, namely corporate cohesiveness (IHSM 1991). It is held that a more formalised system of appraisal such as the IPR is a tool for forward planning, monitoring and reviewing of individual performance. It seeks to adopt a systematic approach to improving the effectiveness and efficiency of the job performer by motivating the individual in his or her work, and ensuring that individuals' goals for a set period of time are clearly defined. It allows for regular feedback to be given on how the individual is performing and for adjusting and redefining the next phase of the on-going process. It can also be used to highlight those areas where the job holder needs further training to enable a key object to be met satisfactorily (Rowe 1992).

It is contended the IPR is a system that seeks to help each job holder in the NHS to:

• be clear about what job performance is expected of him or her;

• receive feedback from the manager in the light of this;

• understand how his or her own job ties up with, and affects, the work of others.

Within those case study areas that had introduced a formalised performance management system in the form of the IPR, it was found that it was tailored to meet the specific needs of each area and the individual specialty within it. The unique elements of each system will be brought out later in the chapter. However, there were a number of features to this system which were common across the case study areas and these can be outlined as follows.

The personal preparation sheet/checklist
Approximately two weeks before the IPR interview, line managers are expected to request their staff to undertake an extensive self-appraisal by completing a form known as a personal preparation checklist. This form is used by each nurse to consider a number of key areas which are then discussed fully in the interview with their immediate line manager.

Broadly speaking, the four major areas that nurses are asked to think about are:

• their job, its main purpose and the key tasks that enable them to fulfil that purpose. A nurse is normally expected to identify between two and five key tasks using their own job description as their starting point;

• their performance to date against the objectives which have been previously set including whether they have achieved them and if not, the reasons why. If a nurse has not had objectives agreed in the past, they are expected to consider their performance of key tasks. An objective is defined as an important activity and outcome crucial to the effective performance of the job;

• what their aims and aspirations are, both in their present post and for the future. These can then be raised with the line manager at the meeting with a view to incorporating them into the nurse's objectives;

• what their future objectives ought to be, taking into account their key tasks for the coming year, performance to date, aims and aspirations as well as their overall departmental objectives.

At the end of this self-appraisal, each individual nurse is expected to draw together their thoughts on these issues and be fully prepared to discuss them with their line manager.

How does the manager prepare for the IPR?
In parallel, managers are also expected to prepare for the IPR interview by completing an appraiser preparation sheet. This is used to help them consider what they see each individual nurse's key tasks to be, their current performance against any set objectives and what they see the nurse's objectives to be for the next year to ensure they fit in with the overall objectives and plans of the department.

The IPR interview
The next stage of the IPR process is the actual interview between the individual nurse and the immediate line manager. The interview should be an open discussion between the nurse and the line manager regarding the four key areas they have been asked to think about. The nurse is normally encouraged to undertake at least 50 per cent of the talking. After this discussion, they are expected to:

- identify and agree the key tasks of the post;

- consider current performance, against objectives if these have previously been set, taking into account any support which the appraisee may need;

- incorporate as far as possible the appraisee's aims and aspirations in their present post and the future;

- set objectives for the following period, taking into account the overall plans and objectives for the department, the appraisee's performance to date and their aims and aspirations;

- agree any action that needs to be taken by either party to facilitate the objectives being met. This may include training for an appraisee in order for an objective to be met;

- agree whether there is a need to review progress at an interim stage.

At the end of the interview, the line manager is expected to agree a date in the next five working days to sign off the checksheet which is a record of the points covered in the IPR interview.

In most cases, the nurse and the line manager will meet to sign the checksheet. The written list of objectives and the plan for how they are to be achieved the actions is then countersigned by the grandparent. The word 'grandparent' is used to describe the nurse's manager's manager. The function of the grandparent is to oversee the process (making sure it happens, is being taken seriously and that reasonable judgements are being formed). The manager is then expected to make two photocopies of the checksheet for the nurse and themselves and send the original to the personnel department, together with a note of any action that needs to be taken in relation to training.

However, on some occasions, the nurse may not agree with what is contained in the checksheet. In such cases, the individual nurse is expected to tick the appropriate box denoting this disagreement on the checksheet. In such cases, the individual nurse has the right to appeal to the grandparent. On occasions, the grandparent may be required in a counselling role where there is substantial disagreement. Ideally, the grandparent should have some personal contact with the individual and be aware of their main objectives. If the nurse and the line manager are unable to resolve the issue, it is possible for the nurse to carry it further by use of the employer's grievance procedure.

Monitoring

During the following twelve-month period, the manager and job holder should hold regular discussions to monitor and review progress. Some of these will be formal meetings, and will result in objectives and implementation plans being changed because outside circumstances have changed someone moved the goalposts. Some meetings will be informal perhaps just a phone call to keep in touch and provide support, coaching or counselling. This is known in IPR as the monitoring process.

Major performance review

IPR should involve 'no end of year surprises'. At the end of the twelve-month period, the final IPR stage comes into play known as the Major Performance Review. In contrast to most appraisals, where the manager sits in judgement, IPR enables the job holder themselves to be clear about whether objectives have been met and, if not, the reasons. The major performance review should be viewed as a stock-take, and it allows better plans to be made for next year.

The method of assessing nursing staff

The study found that three of the six nurse employers had introduced the individual performance review as a way of formally appraising their nursing staff. These nurse employers were case studies B, D and E. However, further investigation revealed that even within these employers, implementation had only been partial.

In case study B, nursing staff in only one of three nursing specialties, the care of the elderly directorate, were actually being appraised using the IPR. Within the other two specialties of midwifery and community examined within this employer, interviews with management revealed there was no formal performance management system in operation apart from that required by statute. The Nurses, Midwives and Health Visitors Act 1979 and the Nurses, Midwives and Health Visitors Act 1992 lays down the statutory requirement that midwives should be regularly supervised. This legislation lays down the role of the Local Supervisory Authority (in most cases the Regional Health Authority (RHA)), which is expected to delegate the supervision of midwives to small teams of specially appointed local supervisors of midwives, normally the Director of Midwifery Services and senior midwifery colleagues in the area. The role of the supervisors is to safeguard and improve the quality of care for the childbearing woman and her baby by continuously monitoring the practice of all midwives practising within the area, whether they are employed by the NHS, other employers or are self-employed. The clinical practice of each midwife is monitored by the supervisor at least annually and appropriate records are kept.

Similarly, managers within the community unit explained there was no formal performance management system in operation for their nursing staff. As one manager working within this unit explained, 'we do not have an official appraisal system but I talk to staff and ask them how they are getting on and whether they are happy'. Nursing staff working within this unit confirmed that no formal appraisal took place and also contended that there was no regular informal appraisal either. The director of personnel responsible for the three nursing specialties within this employer confirmed that there was no formal trust-wide performance management system in operation. She stated that the only thing that could be regarded as a form of assessment comprised 'informal chats with nursing staff by sisters on how they were doing'.

In case study D, both the specialties of surgery and midwifery had recently introduced the IPR as a system of formally appraising their nursing staff. However, the implementation of it to date had been partial.

The director of nursing for surgery explained that she had introduced IPR in her clinical directorate in 1991. In addition to the standard features of the IPR outlined earlier, there was an additional section upon which nursing staff were appraised. This was called the performance section and both the individual nurse being appraised and the line manager undertaking the appraisal were expected to give a rating of A (above average), B (average) or C (below average) to denote how they thought this individual nurse was performing the ten key tasks outlined in this section. The ten tasks were:

- the extent to which a nurse updated his/ her clinical knowledge;

- the ability to work successfully within a team to achieve the goals of the unit;

- how responsive and sensitive a nurse was to the needs of patients and visitors;

- communication skills, both oral and written;

- organisational skills including the ability to plan, prioritise and cope with 'crises';

- decision-making skills including being able to make timely and appropriate actions, analysis and judgement;

- the ability to be adaptable and cope with change;

- the strength of commitment including taking responsibility as appropriate for the grade;

- teaching skills, in particular the ability to bring the best out in people;

- management skills as appropriate for the grade.

However, according to the director of nursing services for surgery:

> This system of assessment has not percolated down to all levels. In the two years I have been here we have had an IPR of all nursing staff down to E grades. But no wards have managed to appraise their nursing staff down to grade A.

This was confirmed by a ward manager in surgery who revealed that only staff down to grade E had been appraised using the IPR. Unfortunately, this ward manager's own IPR had last been undertaken two years ago and she was still awaiting her IPR for last year. She continued that there was an intention to appraise formally all their nursing staff, including their unqualified nursing staff, using IPR. However, at present such unqualified nursing staff were only informally assessed

> ... by just working with them and continually assessing them on a day-to-day basis based on what their job description says their roles should be and looking at the individual and seeing what they are capable of.

The director of midwifery services within this case study employer explained that the job performance of midwives was assessed in two ways. Firstly, there was the element of statutory supervision which was discussed earlier (see case study B). The second method of assessing midwifery staff was through the IPR. Both the director of midwifery services and the senior midwife within the specialty confirmed that IPR had only recently been introduced. As a result, the system of appraisal had only reached down to ward manager or sister level. However, interviews with staff midwives revealed that they had not been formally appraised but were expecting an IPR to be introduced shortly. At present, their assessment comprised an informal peer appraisal clinical assessment.

In case study E, it was found that only one of the two nursing specialties had a formal performance management system in operation. This area of nursing was care of the elderly. The senior nurse explained that an IPR had been undertaken once a year for the past two years on most nursing staff except for unqualified nursing staff. In addition to the standard features of the IPR system already outlined which entailed a nurse evaluating, in conjunction with her line manager, how well she had met the objectives set from last year, this specialty also expected their qualified nursing staff to evaluate the skills required to carry out these objectives. The job performance was measured using seven written criteria. The importance attached to each was determined by the grade of the nurse. The seven criteria were as follows:

i   organisation and management of work;
ii   supervision of staff and leadership;
iii relationships with patients, their relatives, with immediate colleagues;
iv   ability to communicate both orally and in writing;
v   teaching and training;
vi   ability to contribute, develop and carry out new ideas and methods;
vii problem-solving and decision-making skills.

The extent to which a system of appraisal was implemented was greater than in the other nursing area within this case study employer. Within the community unit, there was no formal performance management system in operation. However, the senior nurse within this unit explained that there was an intention to introduce the IPR sometime in the future. At present, senior nurses within this unit were undertaking a two-day training course on how to implement this system effectively. However, the personnel manager of this unit felt that they 'were a long way from introducing the IPR'. When questioned about how nursing staff were currently appraised, she explained that locality managers (senior nurses working in the community unit) appraised their staff informally by having regular meetings with the staff but she was unsure as to their commitment in undertaking this task. As she explained, 'some managers do it [undertake an informal review] because they choose to and some managers would rather not'.

Leading management personnel in the three remaining nurse employers of case studies A, C and F said their was an intention to introduce the IPR as a way of formally appraising their nursing staff as soon as possible.

In case study A, none of the three nursing specialties studied had introduced a system of formal appraisal such as the IPR. However, in 1987 a policy statement was introduced which stated the employer's intention to introduce a system of appraisal for all staff employed by them. This states:

> The Authority regards performance review as an integral part of the broad management process, not as a mere technique. The Authority therefore looks to its managers and staff to give their wholehearted support to performance review as a means of ensuring that their undoubted commitment to their profession, skills and health services are best directed to the delivery of the highest quality of care to patients and clients. It is an essential part of specifying

organisational objectives, reviewing progress and performance and the part played by the Authority and its employees in achieving specified objectives. Appraisal is therefore part of organisational and individual development. It is a normal feature of managerial/supervisory responsibilities, part of the Authority's explicit expectation about how the employees it entrusts to managers/ supervisors are managed. The Authority fully supports performance review and its implications and intends to extend its application throughout all appropriate levels in the District.

Currently, the method of appraising nursing staff tended to be extremely informal. The personnel manager responsible for the mental health unit explained that the only assessment that they undertook constituted a form of peer review involving

... a day to day evaluation of the work nurses have to perform undertaken by their fellow nurses ... nurses are accountable and responsible for their own work. They discuss their work with fellow nurses at the same level and are then overseen by the charge nurse.

Again, in both the general and community units, managers explained that at present the system of appraisal tended to be very informal. According to the director of personnel in the community unit this entailed 'sisters gathering their staff together and telling them how they are doing ... [but] some don't even do this'.

In case study C, managers acknowledged that in the absence of IPR their midwifery staff were not being systematically appraised. Perhaps surprisingly, both managers revealed that any judgement on a particular midwife's performance would only be brought to light if the midwife herself expressed some concern over an aspect of her job role. Hence, if midwives did not identify any difficulties they had in their job, then management assumed they were undertaking their tasks satisfactorily and they were unlikely to be appraised even in an informal way. Similarly, within the care of the elderly specialty, there was no systematic appraisal system currently in operation. According to the senior nurse of the specialty 'we are currently reviewing our appraisal system. We recognise not having one is a problem.' This senior nurse continued that there was a very informal and ad-hoc appraisal undertaken by ward managers on staff nurses and below which constituted a discussion with the appropriate member of the nursing staff on how they felt they were performing in the job. On the other hand, 'ward managers were not appraised in any way at the moment'.

In case study F, neither of the two nursing specialties of mental health and general medical had introduced a formal performance management for their nursing staff. According to the director of nursing services of the mental health unit, a successful pilot of the IPR (referred to as the Staff

Performance Review (SPR) within this particular employer) had been undertaken in 1993 and there were plans under way to introduce it by April 1994. According to the Hospital Staff Performance Review Handbook, the SPR is intimately linked to the more effective delivery of service to patients. The hospital's mission statement states that:

> The Hospital and all its staff aim to provide the best care, cure and comfort possible to the local community.
>
> We aim to achieve this through the following:
>
> • recognition of the dignity of individuals;
>
> • by examples and education to encourage healthy lifestyles;
>
> • to employ the best available practices in clinical care and management disciplines to ensure the most efficient use of resources;
>
> • close cooperation with other caring agencies.

The ward manager of the mental health unit confirmed that the SPR system of appraisal was about to be introduced in the near future. At present, the only time her nursing staff were even informally assessed was when she occasionally evaluated her staff 'whilst on the job in the tasks they were doing'. Written notes of such informal appraisals were kept by her but she only offered oral feedback to individual nursing staff if they asked for it themselves.

Within the general medical unit, managers reiterated their intention to introduce a formal performance management system by the middle of 1994. A senior nurse explained that personnel were currently devising a training course for people who will have to undertake such assessments. However, at present, the form of appraisal tended to be informal and involved a day-to-day evaluation of how each nursing staff member was performing in the job.

The difficulties associated with introducing the individual performance review (IPR)

As we have seen, the introduction of a performance management system for nursing staff in case studies B, D and E has not been without its difficulties. What precisely were the problems that employers faced in introducing a formal system of assessment?

In case study B, only one of the three specialties, care of the elderly, had introduced the IPR as a system of appraising their nursing staff. A ward manager working in this specialty explained some of the older unqualified nursing staff preferred a more informal process of appraisal where they were told by their ward manager about how they were performing in the job. This was because they associated the degree of formality involved in going into the ward manager's office for a meeting to discuss their progress with being disciplined. As the ward manager explained, 'previously they had only been told off for what they didn't do, not praised for what they did do'.

In case study D, both the specialties had introduced a formal performance management system to appraise their nursing staff. Within midwifery, the senior midwife explained that they had had two major problems in effectively implementing the IPR. Firstly, ward managers had expressed concern that the IPR would take up a substantial element of their work time if they were expected to undertake it for all their staff. This was further compounded by the problem that these people had not received any training on how to implement the IPR and as a result expressed a distinct lack of confidence in being able to undertake such appraisals effectively.

Within case study E, problems had arisen, largely of the employer's own making, regarding the effective implementation of a performance management system. Firstly, they had forgotten to provide enough space for an action plan to be agreed on the appraisal form and secondly the senior nurses and ward managers had received only a day of training on how to undertake the IPR effectively. This was felt to be insufficient for them to feel fully confident in carrying this task out effectively.

What were the problems that faced those employers that had not yet introduced the IPR as a formal way of assessing their nursing staff?

In case study A, managers in the three nursing specialties studied acknowledged there had been undue delay in introducing a performance management system for nursing staff. The director of personnel for the community unit explained that this was because senior nursing staff had not received the necessary training to be able to undertake appraisals using the IPR effectively. This training was expected to be extensive, lasting a total of four days and would involve all senior nurses involved in appraising their nursing staff. Once this programme of training had been completed, it was expected the IPR would be introduced by the middle of 1994.

In case study C, neither of the two nursing specialties had introduced a formal system of appraisal. In midwifery, both the director of midwifery services and one of the senior midwives confirmed that the IPR would be introduced by September 1994. According to the senior midwife, its introduction had been delayed because of the concern expressed by many senior midwives regarding the time-consuming nature of undertaking an IPR for all their nursing staff.

In case study F, the ward manager of the mental health unit acknowledged that informal appraisals were inadequate as a means of assessing their nursing staff because they could potentially be subjective and based on no commonly agreed criteria. Moreover, she identified informal appraisals as being potentially unfair because only those staff who worked on the same shifts as herself had the opportunity to be appraised. Those nursing staff working on the night shift were unlikely to be appraised because they did not work the same shifts as the ward manager.

The views of nursing staff on how they were assessed

This part of the chapter reports the views of nursing staff on how they were currently assessed and what they thought of the introduction of a formal performance management system. In the first case, we looked at the views of nursing staff working in those specialties which had actually introduced such a system.

In case study B, only one of the three specialties studied, care of the elderly, had introduced a formal system of appraisal. Staff nurses working within this unit reported that since the beginning of last year they were having one staff appraisal a year. However, opinions as to whether the system was beneficial were mixed. One staff nurse was not convinced that this type of appraisal undertaken by one's immediate line manager was conducive to good working relations. She expressed concern that such an appraisal created 'a delicate situation where the truth is not always spoken as you have to work with her every day'. This nurse clearly identified that the climate in which such an appraisal was undertaken was crucial to understanding how effective it would be. On the other hand, a staff nurse felt the IPR system of appraisal was very constructive and was pleased with the opportunity that it provided for her to have a formal meeting with her immediate line manager to discuss the objectives that she had to meet and hoped to achieve in the following year. She also felt it helped iron out any difficulties she had with regard to her actual job performance. Only one of the two unqualified nursing staff had had a formal appraisal in the form of an IPR. This person was in favour of the system because she felt it allowed her to get her to talk about her job in an open way and she believed this would be helpful for her when she set goals for the future.

In case study D, we saw that although both the specialties had introduced a formal system of appraisal, it had yet to reach nursing staff below the level of ward manager. Those that had been appraised using the IPR were satisfied with such a system of appraisal whereas those had not received an IPR were extremely dissatisfied about how they were currently assessed.

A staff nurse explained how not being appraised using the IPR denied her the opportunity to identify her strengths and weaknesses.

> I think you should be [formally assessed] because you need to be told how you can improve and also be told about the things you do well. I think you should be praised because a lot of people get demoralised if they do not get praised for anything. And things get out of hand whereas if they had been assessed in the first place you could have sorted out the problem much easier. You get nurses who have been doing the same job for 20 years and there are things they have been doing wrong for all these years. Then they get told to change and its such a shock and upheaval to them ... somebody should have told them a long time ago.

Another staff nurse echoed the dissatisfaction about not having a formal assessment.

> I've had one informal chat about my future career prospects and my performance but I haven't had a formal one. I know I'm supposed to have one. It's just a question of whoever is supposed to be doing it, actually doing it. I know it would be useful in the sense that not only do I find out how I am doing but also other people tell me how I am doing. If there's a problem, I'm not very good at coming forward. If there was a formal assessment, you can actually bring this up and don't feel guilty talking about it. You can get feedback from it and make changes.

Both the unqualified members of nursing staff working within this specialty said they had not been formally appraised using the IPR. Indeed they were under the misconception that the IPR system of appraisal was just for qualified members of nursing staff. Moreover, they were unaware that their job performance was informally assessed on the basis of their job descriptions as outlined earlier by the ward manager.

On the other hand, although unqualified nursing staff working within midwifery were not formally assessed either, they had no wish to see a formal appraisal system in operation. They felt it unnecessary when there was little opportunity for career development at their level.

> I don't think it matters now because the grading is already done. As long as the head of your ward feels you are doing the job, I don't see why they should assess you, particularly if you are not going to get any more money.

Both the director of midwifery services and the senior nurse acknowledged that all staff midwives would be appraised using the IPR. However, they disagreed with the proposal that IPR ought to encompass unqualified nursing staff. They felt that it was inappropriate to utilise such a tool in assessing unqualified nursing staff and favoured the present method of assessment which involved an 'informal chat' with such members and finding out

> ... how they are getting on ... As well as this chat, the ward manager should be regularly evaluating how the nursing auxiliaries are performing in their daily tasks.

These managers felt that the IPR was particularly inappropriate for use with unqualified nursing staff because the current system of assessment was already based upon written criteria from their job descriptions and written records kept of the assessment. This was the only specialty studied that had a fully operational and clearly-defined formal system of appraising unqualified nursing staff. The work of all unqualified nursing staff working in the maternity unit was assessed at regular intervals of every six months, based upon a list of twenty tasks in which they were expected to be competent. These included learning techniques to avoid the risk of infection, the correct cleaning procedure of labour wards and bed-making practices, the correct lifting techniques, undertaking urine tests, bathing mothers, effective handling of patients and visitors, dealing with telephone enquiries, and cleaning equipment. What is interesting to note is that neither nursing auxiliary could recall ever being formally assessed in the manner outlined.

In case study E, one of the two nursing specialties, care of the elderly, had introduced a formal system of appraisal. The interviews with nursing staff working in the care of the elderly unit revealed that all qualified nursing staff were appraised using the IPR. Whilst these nursing staff expressed satisfaction at how they were assessed, nursing auxiliaries who had been assessed informally expressed dissatisfaction. Both of them favoured a more formal appraisal system by which their work could be properly evaluated.

What were the views of nursing staff in those employers and specialties where a formal performance management system had not been introduced? In case study A, it was found that none of the three specialties had introduced a formal system of appraisal. Most of the nursing staff working within these three specialties favoured the introduction of a more formalised system of appraisal. A ward manager explained that the last time he had been assessed was four years ago when a formal appraisal system called the 'mutual performance assessment' was used. He explained that this had collapsed due to the reorganisation currently underway in the NHS.

> The IPR is something that has not really taken off here. I think this is because there has been such a lot of upheaval in the hospitals here in the last three or

four years, managers have come and gone and the system of appraisal has disintegrated.

Similarly, unqualified nursing staff within this specialty highlighted the inadequate nature of assessment when they revealed that neither had had a formal appraisal in their period of employment within this unit. One of them stated that the only occasions someone commented on her work was when 'I did anything wrong. Then someone would tell me, otherwise I assume I am performing my tasks satisfactorily'.

All the qualified nursing staff within the general unit confirmed that no formal performance management system was in place. The unqualified nursing staff working on this unit stated they had no knowledge of how they were currently assessed. However, there were mixed feelings about the possible introduction of a more formalised system of appraisal. One of them was unsure about the underlying purpose of introducing such a system of appraisal. On the other hand, the other unqualified member of nursing staff was more in favour and felt there was an advantage in being formally assessed. 'If you're not doing the job right, you should be assessed and told about it. Nobody's ever told me anything'.

The health visitors within the community unit all explained they had not had a formal appraisal. One health visitor reported that she had not been appraised for over three years. The only form of appraisal that did take place was a form of peer appraisal whereby the line manager (known as the locality manager in the community unit) would accompany a particular health visitor whilst she was undertaking her clinical duties visiting patients. Apart from this, health visitors had the option of discussing any difficulties they had in carrying out their tasks with their immediate line manager at the weekly conference. Most felt they would benefit from a clearly defined system of appraisal because 'it would be very useful for everyone to understand how they are doing'.

In the two nursing specialties in case study B where there was no formal system of appraisal in operation, the feeling amongst nursing staff was that a formal appraisal system would be worthwhile.

In case study C, none of the specialties had introduced a formal performance management system to assess their nursing staff. The dominant view amongst nursing staff within this case study was dissatisfaction at the lack of a formal assessment and a belief that a more systematic appraisal would be of benefit to their career development.

All the midwifery staff within this employer confirmed that their job performance was not formally assessed using a system of appraisal such as the IPR. However, there was an element of statutory supervision which was discussed earlier. Both senior and staff midwives felt strongly that a formal appraisal system which included an identification of their learning needs was necessary. A midwife sister explained that, 'you should have an assessment yearly so that if you're doing something that could be improved upon or if you have a little light shining away that could be nurtured, it can be pointed out to you'.

Similarly, another staff midwife stated her preference for having a formal appraisal system and also pointed out the dangers of not having one when she explained, 'if it's going to give you some sort of career development. At present, it's who you know than what you know that counts.

However, unqualified nursing staff were more hesitant about the advantages that may accrue as a result of the introduction of a formal performance management system. Neither of the two unqualified nursing staff working in midwifery were in favour of having a formal appraisal system.

None of the nursing staff working in the specialty of care of the elderly had had a formal appraisal. All except one declared their preference for having one. As an unqualified nursing staff member explained, 'If you're doing well, then you should be told, right?' Similarly, a charge nurse expressed the views of most of the qualified nursing staff when she pointed to the advantages of a more formalised system of assessment:

> You need advice, encouragement and criticism. It should enable you to keep the good and weed out the bad. But management is so busy setting themselves up first before anybody else here. There's been so many re-organisations at the top in order to feather their nest prior to becoming a Trust ... maybe they'll 're-vet' the masses next year when they're cosy. That's the way it looks round here. I know its a cynical view.

Opinion on the lack of a formal system of assessment was divided amongst nursing staff working within the community unit in case study E. Some health visitors questioned whether those managers that would have to appraise them were in touch with the latest clinical developments in their field and therefore competent in undertaking the task effectively. Others regarded such an appraisal as a threat to their independence and felt it questioned their ability to work unsupervised. In the absence of such a system, only a minority of health visitors and none of the unqualified nursing staff interviewed in this unit had even been informally appraised. This informal appraisal involved an on-the-job clinical assessment by the locality manager 'overseeing the work of a health visitor whilst she was visiting families'. However, the health visitors argued that such an informal appraisal was very subjective and was undertaken only once every two or three years. Only one health visitor working in this unit was satisfied with how she was currently appraised. She was the only one who seemed to have a regular appraisal where a written record was kept. She explained the form this appraisal took as follows:

> We have a three-monthly review. We discuss our families with our manager. If she is worried about what I was doing, she would discuss this with me. We have a chance to say how we are getting on and what we see as our future plans. If you are concerned about anything, you can normally arrange another meeting with your manager to discuss this.

The unqualified members of nursing staff working within this unit explained they had no knowledge of how they were assessed. Both favoured the introduction of a formal appraisal system where they would find out how they were performing in their job. One unqualified member of the nursing staff stated that:

> It would be nice to have an appraisal. At least you would know how you are performing and it would give you an insight into whether people are satisfied or dissatisfied and where you can make improvements.

In case study F, neither of the two specialties studied had introduced a formal performance management system to assess their nursing staff. The interviews with some of the qualified nursing staff working in the mental health unit revealed that they were informally assessed and they thought this was unsatisfactory. This informal assessment comprised:

> ... a ward manager asking you how you are getting on. I think they have a meeting about once a month about the work on the ward. They're so busy here that people don't have time to sit down and talk to you.

However, there were mixed feelings as to whether a more formalised system of assessment such as the IPR would be of benefit to them. Some felt it would be beneficial because 'if it helps someone's level of competence, makes them more experienced, then it must be a good thing.' On the other hand, other members of the nursing staff thought it would be disadvantageous because 'I'm not happy with the manager who will be assessing me ... He hardly meets me and so cannot really comment. I think it should be someone who knows what I do'.

Both the unqualified members of the nursing staff working on this ward outlined how they were informally assessed. One unqualified nurse explained how she had regular discussions with her ward manager about 'what she can and cannot do'. On the whole, this occurred every three to six months but was dependent upon whether the ward manager 'had the time'. The other unqualified member of nursing staff was a Health Care Assistant (HCA). She argued that she was very dissatisfied with the way she was assessed and would have preferred a more formal and regular assessment which 'would give people encouragement to think about what they're doing and where they're going'.

In the general medical unit, the senior nurse explained that informal assessments were no longer an adequate means by which to evaluate nursing staff:

> As long as a nurse does not make a mistake, it is assumed she is performing satisfactorily ... It's terrible. I couldn't believe when I first came here in 1987 that I was told I was doing nothing wrong for years. A formal appraisal system is essential as a developmental tool for nursing staff. So it's been a long time coming and is very welcome.

The sister from one of the wards of the general medical unit explained how 'difficult it is to assess the work of an individual nurse because it becomes very subjective ... that's my personal view'. She continued that everyone would benefit if a formal appraisal system were introduced for at present 'it constituted an ad hoc, subjective, day-to-day evaluation of a nurse's performance'.

However, she did stress that if the IPR system of appraisal was to be implemented effectively, staff involved in appraising would have to receive the appropriate training.

All the qualified nursing staff interviewed who worked within the general medical unit expressed their wish to see the introduction of a more formalised system of assessment such as the IPR. Similarly, the unqualified nursing staff also stated their support for such a system.

Summary and conclusion

The interviews with managers, coupled with the consultation of the appropriate policy documents and interviews with nursing staff revealed that only three of the six case study areas had introduced the IPR as a system of appraising their nursing staff. The remaining three case study areas operated informal appraisal systems undertaken at irregular intervals on undefined criteria. However, all three areas did declare their intention to introduce a more formalised appraisal system in the form of the IPR by the middle of 1994. Even within the three case study areas where it had been introduced, implementation had been partial. In particular, there were three serious problems. First, the system of appraisal had not been introduced across all the nursing specialties within each employer. Secondly, it had yet to reach all nursing staff falling within the clinical nursing grading structure, with nursing staff below the grade of ward manager rarely being appraised. Thirdly, there were problems in actually carrying it out effectively. Some nursing staff expressed concern about how an appraisal system which involved the appraiser and apprai-see in such an open relationship would affect their working relationships. In particular, clinical nursing staff below the grade of ward manager often perceived those managing them less as nurses and more as mana-gers. As a result, this perception often discouraged the very openness that IPR demands. In those areas where there was no formal appraisal system, the job performance of nursing staff was either not appraised at all or was appraised informally. Where job performance was assessed informally, not all staff working within such a ward were appraised and even those irregularly so, and on no commonly stated criteria. Unqualified nursing staff tended not be appraised in any formal way whatsoever. Again those that were appraised informally, and not many were aware that they were, had little idea on what basis their performance was assessed. A key issue to emerge was the need to accompany a formal method of appraisal with appropriate training for those who were to be involved in undertaking such appraisals.

The dissatisfaction regarding the slow progress towards implementing a formal system of appraisal such as the IPR was as great amongst white staff as it was amongst ethnic minority staff. Hence, the effect of a lack of appraisal system was not of more concern to nurses of ethnic minority origin than white nursing staff. Rather the problem regarding the implementation of a formal system of appraisal was an issue of concern to the whole of the nursing profession and this has clear implications with regard to their career development. Without a formal system of assessment, decisions that are made with regard to promotion, limited as they are in the current climate, will be seen as being subjective. However, such decisions, if not based upon objective and clearly stated criteria, may be increasingly viewed as potentially discriminatory by ethnic minority nursing staff.

5 Training and development

Training and development has been defined as 'the spectrum of activities aimed at improving the human capital within an organisation' (Storey and Sisson 1993). Training and development or human resource development (HRD) as it is increasingly known, is regarded as a major component of human resource management (HRM). It is contended that training and development are crucial for two inter-related reasons. First, an organisation that fails to train its employees will find itself dependent upon the external labour market and will consequently regard its current employees only as a cost. Secondly, the organisation that trains its staff is more likely to engage in the other aspects of HRM which will in turn help to make the employees feel more valued.

The management of training and development is normally seen as a cycle of logical steps as shown by Figure 5.1.

Figure 5.1   The training and development cycle

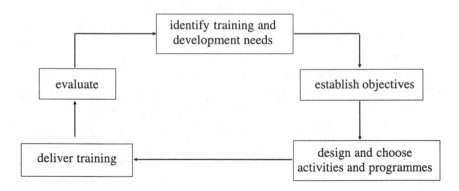

(taken from Storey and Sisson 1993: 157)

The cycle ideally commences with the identification of training needs. This process of 'training needs analysis' involves an assessment of the gap between desired levels of knowledge, skills, and competencies and the actual pattern of current levels. The usual recommended approach is to focus in turn, on the organisation as a whole, the department or unit, and then the individual. In this way one is led from an assessment of the overall organisation trajectory and its future plans, down through the implications of these plans for sectional skill needs, and then on to the disaggregated individual training needs. This information can be collected either through direct observation or through performance appraisals. The second step is to identify learning objectives. This means stating what capabilities a trainee will be able to demonstrate following completion of the training. The third step is the design and choice of activities which are related to the selection of learning methods deemed most appropriate to meet the learning objectives. The fourth step is the implementation stage where the training is delivered and the final stage is the evaluation of the training undertaken (Storey and Sisson 1993: 156-158).

The training and development of nursing staff
Training opportunities for clinical nursing staff are an issue of increasing importance within the NHS today. It is held that the need for nursing staff to undertake further training after qualification is important for three major reasons. First, by ensuring that they update their clinical nursing skills at regular intervals, they will be more likely to continue to deliver a high quality of patient care. Related to this point are the benefits that accrue to the employers themselves from such an effective delivery of care. Finally, training is of crucial importance to nursing staff and their chances for further career development.

Recent developments such as the 'Project 2000' and the Post-Registration Education and Practice (PREP) recommendations have arguably been the UKCC's most wide-ranging contributions to the growing professionalism of nursing (Mangan 1993a). The report on Project 2000 undertaken by the UKCC called for a new type of nurse, a 'registered practitioner', who is expected ultimately to replace the previous two grades of registered nurse and enrolled nurse and will have a similar status to that held by registered nurses today. The registered practitioner will receive support and advice from specialist practitioners who have been promoted from registered practitioner status by virtue of post-registration qualifications. The registered practitioner will be expected to take responsibility for the care of patients and, in this way, the UKCC hopes to increase the amount of care given by qualified nursing staff rather than unqualified staff. However, the UKCC has recognised that registered practitioners will not be able to provide all the care patients require and have consequently proposed that there should be a health care assistant (HCA), who will work under the direct supervision of the registered practitioner and who, it is hoped, will take over much of the nursing auxiliary's role (Gatley 1993; UKCC 1986).

Among the major PREP recommendations was the need to have a period of support for all newly registered practitioners to consolidate the competencies of learning outcomes achieved at registration. To ensure that each nurse has kept pace with developments in their particular field of nursing, the PREP proposals included several statutory requirements including the need for all nurses, midwives and health visitors to demonstrate that they have maintained and developed their professional knowledge and competence. During the three years leading to periodic re-registration, all practitioners are expected to complete a period of study or provide evidence of appropriate professional learning. A minimum of five days study leave every three years must be undertaken by every registered practitioner.

It has been held that both these developments were part of the UKCC's remit to protect the patient by regulating the profession. Until these changes, routes towards gaining diplomas and degrees depended upon nurses being able to get the time and the funding from their employers. As a consequence of limited resources this has become increasingly difficult. Similarly, other nursing staff who were willing to fund the courses themselves had found that they struggled to commit the time needed to undertake the training because of the low staffing levels and high workload. As a result, it is argued that the NHS reforms that have brought the division of responsibilities for health care between purchasing authorities and provider units also heralded opportunities for the development of individual staff (Mangan 1993b). Many provider units have seen that it was in their interests to demonstrate that 'their' nurses comply with PREP recommendations as an indicator of the quality of the service they had to offer. Hence, nurses and those who employ them are increasingly finding that the governing body of the profession, the UKCC, now demands that nursing staff undertake further training if they are to continue to practice as registered nurses.

Broadly speaking, there are two major ways that an individual nurse can apply to get on a training course. The first method entails a nurse becoming aware of a particular training opportunity from information she has obtained. This nurse would then approach her ward manager informally to discuss the possibility of attending the course. If the ward manager was favourable to the opportunity, the nurse would complete a study leave form which would be countersigned by the ward manager supporting her request. This study leave form would then be sent to the senior nurse of the specialty for final approval. The second method of application entailed the ward manager undertaking the lead role in identifying a suitable training option for a particular nurse. The ward manager would approach the relevant nurse and encourage her to take up the particular training opportunity she had identified. Clearly, if this method of allocating training opportunities is to work effectively and equitably, it is reliant upon the ward manager being aware of the learning needs of her nursing staff before making any recommendations.

As we found out in the preceding chapter on staff appraisals, this has not always been the case. The individual performance review (IPR) was not fully operational for clinical nursing staff. For most nursing staff, the learning needs and the associated training opportunities were not identified systematically. This has potentially serious implications for equal opportunities and the fair and equitable allocation of training opportunities to all nursing staff.

Chapters 11 and 13 contain detailed information from the postal survey of over 14,000 members of nursing staff on training opportunities. In particular, it documents the extent of application to both basic and post-basic training courses, and the level of success enjoyed by particular groups. In addition, it examines the perception of nursing staff on the ease of gaining information on training courses, the ease of getting course fees paid and paid time off to attend courses, and the extent to which nursing staff feel they are encouraged or otherwise by management to go on such courses. Chapter 13 reports the perceptions and experiences of racial discrimination in the allocation of training opportunities.

The findings of these chapters conclude:

- Regardless of ethnicity, qualified nursing and midwifery staff found it easier to access information on further training courses than unqualified auxiliary nursing staff;

- Approximately half of all qualified nursing and midwifery staff found it difficult to get paid time off to attend courses. A smaller proportion of unqualified staff also found this to be the case. Little variation was found between ethnic minority nursing staff and their white counterparts;

- Nearly two-thirds of qualified staff reported that it was difficult to get employers to pay for courses. There were few differences between ethnic minority and white nursing staff;

- Most ethnic minority nursing and midwifery staff believed that within the NHS, and to a lesser extent within their own places of work, racial discrimination in the allocation of training opportunities existed. Most white nursing and midwifery staff did not believe this was the case;

- Approximately a quarter of black and Asian nursing and midwifery staff believed they personally had been racially discriminated against in training opportunities.

In this chapter, based on depth interviews with nursing staff and nursing and personnel management, a number of questions are addressed including:

- did the six nurse employers have written policies on training and career development?

- what were the methods by which nurses and nursing auxiliaries were informed of the availability of training opportunities?

- on what criteria were decisions made to allocate training opportunities to individual nursing staff?

- how satisfied were nursing staff with the current level of training opportunities available to them?

Employer policies on training and development

All six of the nurse employers studied had written policies on training and career development opportunities for nursing staff. Broadly speaking, these policies stated that training served the dual purpose of enabling staff to acquire the skills and knowledge required to perform effectively the tasks and duties for which they were employed and secondly, to develop their individual potential to further their chances of career development.

The methods of informing nursing staff of training opportunities

The methods of informing nursing staff about training opportunities were broadly similar across the six nurse employers. In particular, all six employers used two major ways in which to inform their nursing staff of such opportunities. Firstly, the local colleges of nursing would normally produce a booklet which outlined the courses that it proposed to run for the forthcoming year. This booklet would then be distributed to each individual workbase in the hospitals with the expectation that individual ward managers (and to a lesser degree, the senior nurses within each nursing specialty) would distribute this information to the nursing staff they were responsible for. A second means by which nursing staff were informed of training opportunities was through the distribution of circulars sent by the college of nursing to senior nurses within each specialty. The senior nurses were then expected to distribute this information to their ward managers (or team leaders if they worked in the community unit) who in turn were expected to make this information available to their nursing staff by putting the information on ward notice boards.

In addition to these methods of distributing information about training opportunities, managers in case study B said that nursing staff themselves were expected 'to use their initiative' to keep abreast of any relevant training opportunities in which they may be interested. Furthermore, within this same employer, the director of nursing services of the care of the elderly unit explained that she had encouraged ward managers to have monthly meetings with their nursing staff about their learning needs and aspirations. Similarly, within case study E, the equal opportunities policy of this employer states that:

> Staff should be made aware, by their appropriate line managers, of training and development opportunities available to them, so that no group of employees are disadvantaged.

Consequently, within the care of the elderly specialty in case study E, it was found that nursing staff had a regular six-monthly meeting with the senior nurse of the specialty to plan their training needs based upon their individual performance review. Again, within the mental health specialty of case study F, the ward manager explained that she also sought to have monthly meetings with her staff to discuss any courses they were interested in attending.

Within case study C, employers also made their nursing staff aware of potential training opportunities through the creation of a post of training development officer. This person was given the responsibility of coordinating all in-house training within this employer by constructing a directory containing all the lists of courses available and alongside this the names of each individual nurse and the courses they had been on or had expressed an interest in. This training officer also took responsibility for distributing information on post-basic training courses from the local college of nursing to all wards via senior nurses and ward managers who were expected to put such information up on ward notice-boards.

In the midwifery profession within this employer, monthly meetings were held with staff to discuss the issue of their training needs and requirements. However, it was stressed by managers that midwives were expected to take a personal responsibility in being aware of any courses that were of interest to them. The senior nurse explained that 'we as managers have a responsibility for the professional development of staff, but I always say to staff that they have a responsibility as well'. Similarly, within case study D, the senior nurse manager within the maternity unit outlined a vision that entailed the midwifery staff being more proactive in identifying their training needs. She said that she had only a small role to play in the communication of training opportunities:

> They are professionals in their own right. They can read so we expect them to look at the notice-boards in the hospital on training opportunities. All the in-house training opportunities are circulated to the wards. Midwives have a duty and responsibility to keep themselves up to date. If I think there are particular courses that need to be targeted to certain nurses I will do so.

The decision to grant training opportunities
This part of the chapter explores the basis on which decisions regarding the allocation of particular training opportunities were made and whether these criteria were written down.

An examination of appropriate policy documents revealed that only two of the six nurse employers had written policies which explicitly outlined the criteria by which decisions were to be made regarding the granting of training opportunities. These two employers were case study A and case study B.

In case study A, the criteria, which in reality amounted to broad statements of principle, were contained within the training policy document. This document stated:

> The decision to grant study leave will be .... made with regard to the developmental needs of the individual, the operational and training needs of the Service, the availability of resources, the capacity of the employee to benefit from the particular training event or course of study.

Interviews with management in the three specialties studied within this employer confirmed that in theory they would use these criteria as the basis for decisions regarding the allocation of training opportunities. However, they pointed out that in practice and due to the current climate of limited financial resources, the most important criterion when it came to making such a decision was almost always the limited training budget. As a result, it was common for nursing staff to be expected to pay a substantial part of the course fees as well as have to do the course in their own time. The senior nurse within the community unit explained that:

> ... the criterion [to grant training opportunities] would be set within the division's overall objectives ... it has to meet the needs of their job and the needs of the individual nurse ... the more relevant it is to the job the more we will help to finance the course.

In case study B, the study leave policy of this employer stated that training needs will be identified and agreed 'through individual discussions with employees as part of regular performance appraisal'. However, it has already been established that nursing staff were not regularly appraised and so the learning needs of such staff were in turn not systematically identified. In the absence of a systematic identification of training needs, on what basis were training opportunities allocated?

Interviews with managers suggested that the criteria upon which such decisions were made in practice ranged from the subjective and ad hoc to the more formal. An example of the former was given by the director of nursing services of the community unit who outlined the criteria necessary for enrolled nurses to attend a conversion course:

> The first thing we look at is age. If someone wanted to do a conversion course at 55 it is not cost effective ... We look at service commitment. If someone has been here six months and someone has been here five years, the one that had just arrived would have to wait longer. We also look at their health. The local college of nursing is asking for them to have a medical before to make sure they are fit enough to do the training.

Although these criteria were outlined in relation to conversion courses only, no evidence was provided to suggest that the criteria would be different in relation to getting on other courses. This particular example highlights the potentially unfair nature of decision-making in relation to the allocation of training opportunities.

Within the maternity and care of the elderly units of this nurse employer, the criteria appeared to be more clearly defined (although they were not written down) than those outlined within the community unit. Within the maternity unit, management staff explained that there were three factors upon which requests for training were judged. These were the relevance of the course to the needs of the specialty; the need to ensure equity in the allocation of training opportunities that is the amount of study leave previously undertaken by the nurse compared to other nursing staff; and, finally, the constraints imposed by an increasingly limited financial training budget.

According to the employer's equal opportunities policy another important criterion was the importance of 'providing equal training and career development opportunities for all those who have the desire and potential to progress'. The document went on to state that:

> To ensure that this policy is being carried out, the Trust will monitor numbers of women, minority groups and people with disabilities along with individuals from various age groups who are:
>
> • offered places on internal and external training courses
>
> • who accept and complete internal and external courses.
>
> If the Trust discovers that a particular group is under-represented in training, steps will be taken to address this issue.

However, none of the interviews undertaken with management indicated that they viewed this as an important criterion in determining the allocation of training opportunities.

In the remaining four employers that did not have policies containing written criteria by which to allocate training opportunities, it was found there was a broad range of criteria upon which they based their decisions. However, the decision was almost always influenced in the end by the limited financial budget available for training.

According to managers within the care of the elderly unit in case study C, the decision to grant a particular training opportunity was based upon the extent to which the training course was relevant to the needs of the service and whether it aided the career development of the individual member of nursing staff concerned. This was outlined by the senior nurse within the specialty who stated:

> We look at courses which are relevant to the needs of the service. If someone wanted to do something on paediatrics we would not be interested. It might further your career but what is it going to contribute for our care of the elderly service? [Besides] nurses do not come to me wanting to go on these types of courses. Most want to do courses that will enhance their career development in the area that they are working in.

On the other hand, within the midwifery profession within this employer, the criteria upon which training opportunities were allocated were rather different. The head of midwifery services outlined that the three key criteria she took into account were the need to ensure that training opportunities were allocated equitably to staff across specific areas within maternity; the current skill level of each midwife and whether there was a need to update her clinical skills; and finally seniority, that is, those nurses on senior grades would often have first priority to go on courses.

This employer's equal opportunities policy made an explicit link between training and achieving equal opportunities:

> Training is one of the basic tools in achieving equal opportunities ... It does this by the process of changing attitudes and behaviour as well as by redressing imbalances in knowledge and skills. The authority recognises that there are employees who are under-using their abilities and qualifications. It is expected that the performance appraisal review will be one way of identifying these individuals so that the opportunities can be provided to develop their potential.

To ensure that this process is being undertaken efficiently, the policy went on to state that it was imperative that 'all training is monitored and any imbalances investigated and corrected'. However, as we found out in the preceding chapter, there was no appraisal system in operation and training opportunities were not monitored according to the interviews with managers.

In case study D, the criteria on which the decision to grant training opportunities was made were similar across the two specialties. All the managers involved in this decision-making process explained that as a consequence of limited financial resources any application for training would have to fulfil two key requirements if it was to succeed. The first was the extent to which the course was important to the needs of the specialty and secondly, its relative importance to an individual nurse's personal career development. Senior nurses within both specialties reported that the more the proposed course fulfilled these two criteria the greater the chance of providing financial support and time-off for the individual nurse. The director of nursing services outlined how this procedure worked:

> ... we do expect them to pay a certain percentage themselves. And we also negotiate what proportion of time off I will give them and what they have to fund themselves. I will allow the funding and time off according to how well that fits in with the overall training strategy I have for that patch.

In case study E, decisions as to whether particular requests for training were accepted were based on vague notions of fairness and relevance to the specialty and the individual nurse. The senior nurse within the care of the elderly specialty outlined three criteria that she took into account. These were how long a time a nurse had served here; other training opportunities they had been on; and the relevance of the course to the needs of the specialty. A ward manager placed a greater emphasis on being seen to be fair by linking it to the IPR, but highlighted the difficulties:

> I try to be fair and give everyone a chance of going on courses. I try and link it to the appraisal so that one person does not go on all the courses but it is difficult because it is normally the same people that come and ask to go on all the courses.

Similarly, within the community unit, the granting of training opportunities was explicitly linked to an individual nurse's IPR. However, the senior nurse within this area, explained that despite this it was still difficult not to 'allocate on a first come first served basis' because of the limited training funds available.

Finally, in case study F, managers in both the specialties studied stated there were three factors that they took into account when deciding whether to grant a particular training opportunity to a nurse. These were how relevant it was to the needs of the specialty, the relevance of it to the nurse, and the staffing needs of the ward. The latter meant that if the ward could not operate effectively without the nurse at the time of the training course then she was unlikely to be granted the opportunity. The senior nurse admitted that these were very broad criteria and were open to potential abuse. She acknowledged that ideally to ensure fairness it was important the appraisal system was introduced as soon as possible to ensure that learning needs could be identified systematically and fairly. As she explained:

> We don't have an appraisal system at the moment but we're in the process of creating one which will mean that training requests will come out of the appraisal interview.

All the managers stressed the importance of a limited financial budget as a major constraint in granting training opportunities.

Problems relating to training and development

Interviews with nursing staff in the six employers revealed there was one major problem that they faced in relation to training. This concerned the issue of fairness and equity. The allocation of training opportunities would only be seen to be equitable if a system of identifying the learning needs of each individual nurse had been in operation. The training policy document of case study A stated clearly the role to be played by managers in identifying the training needs of their nursing staff:

> Education and training and development is the responsibility of each manager and supervisor who must ensure that the needs of subordinate staff are kept under constant review and that appropriate action is taken to create personal development programmes, having regard to the priorities, policies and resources of the authority.

Such a view which was also put forward by managers, assumed that the training needs of each individual clinical directorate and the nursing staff working within them had been identified in advance. However, as we found out in the preceding chapter, a formal system of appraisal in the form of the IPR was rarely in operation. Consequently, in practice, the allocation of training opportunities did not occur as it was supposed to. The senior nurse within the community unit in case study A explained that in the absence of a fully operational system of IPR to identify the training needs of each individual nurse the allocation of training opportunities tended to be based upon decisions that were subjective and rarely systematic. The danger of not being seen to be fair in the allocation of training opportunities was evident in the comments made by some ethnic minority nursing staff working for this employer. Some of them strongly suspected that training opportunities were being allocated unfairly. One Indian health visitor explained:

> I wanted to do a degree course but I was told that far too many people from my workplace were already doing degree courses and that they would be understaffed and could not let me do it ... I have also applied for three other courses and been unsuccessful. Some of my white colleagues have been primed, groomed for the jobs they're in now. I have not been groomed.

A white health visitor working in the same health centre also felt that training opportunities were allocated 'to those who shout loudest'.

> I have to fight to go on courses ... I have to be quite pushy which doesn't go down well. I think you have to do something otherwise you don't get on ... I know amongst health visitors ... I've been on numerous study days and colleagues that I've worked with have not been on that many. There are no criteria and it's probably unfair.

The director of personnel within this unit confirmed the ad hoc nature of allocating training opportunities when she explained that:

> The initial criterion is if there is a demonstrated need for an individual nurse to go on a particular training course. Once this has been met by everyone who must attend getting on the course it is normally on the basis of first come first served ... we do try and maintain a balance but some nurses stick their hands up every time ... it's a balancing act between what's in it for them and what's in it for us.

However, it was recognised that a formal system of appraisal was vital to ensure that learning needs were identified and training opportunities equitably allocated. The senior nurse within the general unit explained the need for the IPR to be fully implemented 'to ensure that we look equitably across the board at everyone, whereas up till now it has been a situation where if you would like to go on a course, it was always given to those who shouted loudest'.

To ensure that training opportunities began to be allocated more equitably the director of personnel of the community unit announced there was an intention to monitor applications for training by ethnicity and gender by April 1993.

This difficulty of being seen to be fair in the distribution of training opportunities was made particularly acute in the light of the related problem of limited financial budgets available for training facing these employers. In case study C, it was found that the constraints imposed by a limited financial budget increasingly meant that regardless of the relevance of the course to the needs of the specialty, nursing staff were now almost always expected to make a substantial contribution to course fees and often to undertake it in their own time. The training officer for this employer explained that even when nurses did manage to negotiate to have their fees paid, they still had problems in getting on the course because they couldn't get the time off because of the lack of cover on wards. It was held that training opportunities were now limited in that not everyone could afford to undertake this option of doing it in their own time. Interviews with qualified nursing staff confirmed that the central problem facing them was a lack of financial aid from employers when undertaking courses. A ward manager illustrated the situation in her ward:

> ... courses are very expensive. One day courses the cheapest you are talking about are £35. I have paid up to £90 a day for a course. This is possibly why a lot of midwives do not fund themselves ... they can't afford to go on a study day a month at that sort of price in today's recession.

Although the interviews suggested this was a problem facing all nursing staff, the dangers of not having clearly defined criteria on which decisions are made was graphically illustrated when a number of nurses felt they were being deliberately stopped from going on courses. This could lead to serious problems if ethnic minority nurses began to express the view that they may have been prevented from going on courses because of their ethnicity. An African nurse was particularly concerned that she had managed to get on a conversion course only at the sixth attempt and after she had threatened to leave nursing altogether. Overall, however, lack of training opportunities seemed to be a problem facing all staff irrespective of their ethnicity. A white nurse expressed her dissatisfaction at her lack of opportunities as follows when she argued 'I don't seem to have the right face. A colleague who joined at the same time was offered a course. I asked "what about me"? I've had no encouragement'.

In all six case study areas, it was found that as a result of the limited financial budget available for training, it was becoming increasingly common practice for nurses to register for nursing degrees and pay for the course fees themselves and be expected to do it their own time. This has implications for how individual nursing staff were expected to progress in their careers. A staff nurse in case study B explained how this situation affected her:

> Training opportunities are there but there is a problem with funding. It is very difficult to get seconded. This has been accentuated since we became a Trust ... even if you are really adamant, you have to pay for it yourself and often do it in your own time.

She felt like other nursing staff that this put the onus for developing clinical nursing skills too heavily on the nurses themselves, with the employers not giving them sufficient support in terms of money and time off.

Similarly, a senior nurse in the community unit in case study E explained that this was crucial in whether she supported a training opportunity.

> I can usually only allow one person to go off at any one time. If it was a long course they might have to do some of it in their own time. Nurses are expected to have to pay their own fees but we usually give them paid time off. Lately though it has been suggested that staff should use some of their annual leave to go on courses.

A district nurse confirmed this when she explained 'I've been told there's no time and a lack of funding. I have received no encouragement'. Another district nurse highlighted the dangers involved in allocating training opportunities in the absence of an appraisal system.

> I'm very cross about the allocation system. The way they allocate their time and money seems very unfair because there is no IPR to identify our learning needs. They'd get more out of us if they insisted we train. It's also been noticed that senior nursing staff get more training than field staff.

A ward manager in the mental health unit in case study F stated:

> At the moment everything is money, money, money ... People are very worried about not going over budget. I have been on a counselling course which cost £450 and in that case the hospital provided 50 per cent of the funding but I had to do it in my own time which was one evening a week plus homework, which amounted to a further full day and I got nothing for it at all. This year I wanted to do the second part of the course but have been told there is no funding, no time, nothing at all ... so I was unable to do it.

The problem was the same for staff nurses working in both the mental health and medical units. A staff nurse working in the mental health unit explained how disheartening it was for her:

> They advertise all these courses that you can go on but when it comes down to it and you fill in the form, they turn round and say 'there aren't enough funds or we can't afford to let you take the time of'. It's very disheartening really,

especially when it's to do with things you have to deal with at work ... we have a lot of alcoholics and we don't have any training whatsoever to deal with them.

Similarly, a staff nurse working within the medical directorate highlighted the problem was the same for staff working there:

We're not able to go on courses we would like to because we're needed here. It is really hard to further your career by going on training. There are a lot of things we would like to go on but we can't because we're needed here ... we're stuck in the middle.

Equal opportunities were not a criterion that was explicit in the allocation of training opportunities. According to the personnel manager in the mental health unit:

I don't think we consider equal opportunity issues when it comes to the allocation of training opportunities and we certainly don't monitor them. But my impression is that training opportunities are distributed fairly.

Another central problem which was common across the six nurse employers was in relation to the lack of training opportunities available for unqualified nursing staff.

In case study A, most of the managers across the three units acknowledged the lack of training opportunities for unqualified nursing staff. The personnel manager of the mental health unit explained that they 'do have some training opportunities though not as much as qualified members of staff'. In particular, it was felt there were few opportunities for unqualified members of nursing staff to undertake training which would aid their career development. Indeed, it would be fair to say such staff had no career structure as is commonly understood and the only training opportunities that existed for them were those that consolidated their skills to make them more effective in their present posts. This was confirmed by the senior nurse of the community unit who explained that 'most courses are really to make them more effective in the job they currently do'. However, one note of optimism was the recent introduction of the National Vocational Qualification (NVQ) courses within this employer with levels 1 and 2 being run by the local college of nursing. This encompassed a range of competencies to do with the direct delivery of care including amongst other things communication skills and dealing with patients.

Similarly, in case study B, interviews with managers and unqualified nursing staff in all three specialties revealed that the only course where an unqualified member of nursing staff could develop themselves further was the recently-introduced NVQ course. At present, only a small minority of the unqualified staff had managed to get onto these courses although generally management were supportive and sought to encourage their staff to attend. Only the care of the elderly unit had begun to address the issue of training needs of unqualified staff by establishing an 'auxiliary nurses club' which met informally every month to discuss their training needs. The senior nurse within the community unit explained that qualified staff working on the night shift suffered a similar problem, but felt such staff had chosen to work at night because of their domestic arrangements and therefore probably did not wish to undertake training courses during the day. As she said:

> The evening and night staff have quite young children, the job suits them with the husband coming home from work and them going out to work. It's probably not the time for them to be ambitious and certainly they are not asking to do courses.

Managers within both specialties in case study D acknowledged there were few if any training opportunities for unqualified nursing staff. They all agreed there was none that actually sought to develop their careers. However, there was disagreement about the introduction of the NVQ as a way of alleviating this problem. The director of nursing services thought that the introduction of NVQ may result in the development of career opportunities for unqualified members of staff.

> Most qualified nurses look upon training opportunities as a vehicle toward further career development but the training opportunities that are available for unqualified members of staff are largely to make them more effective in the performance of their current job. I think the NVQ ladder that they can go up is beginning to allow them to develop their skills but it is a very small beginning. Of the hundreds of nursing auxiliaries, only 12 of them have begun the NVQ course. That hardly makes a difference to the overall trend.

On the other hand, the director of midwifery services thought that such courses, as presently designed, were largely useless with regard to work in the midwifery department. She explained that there was already some training in relation to customer care skills, first aid and receptionist courses, but she felt strongly that such unqualified nursing staff should not get involved in the clinical delivery of health care.

> NVQs do not meet the needs of midwifery as a specialty. My health care assistants are never going to be levels 3 and 4 because in midwifery you are either a midwife or you are not ... there are no 'mini-midwives'. You cannot delegate that duty to someone other than possibly to a student midwife.

In case study E, except for the NVQ courses which were now being run up to level 3 in both specialties, there was little in the form of training for unqualified nursing staff. A personnel representative from the community unit explained that this was not surprising since such staff did not expect any.

> At the moment there are not many training opportunities for a nursing auxiliary. For some of them it is a job rather than a career ... that's my subjective view.

In case study F, the senior nurse within the general unit explained that:

> There doesn't seem to be an awful lot around for those that have achieved NVQ qualifications ... particularly for those who may have a specialist interest. I think we have to run more courses for such staff such as front of house training.

Similarly, the ward manager in the mental health unit argued that:

> There aren't enough really ... and those that exist such as the NVQ (which two of her four auxiliaries had attended) are too general oriented and don't meet the needs of unqualified nursing staff working in mental health.

The ward manager working on the general unit explained that, 'there aren't as many [opportunities] as there could be for nursing auxiliaries'. She also highlighted a problem which is of increasing concern amongst unqualified nursing staff who have completed an NVQ course to level 2. There was an assumption that once they had gained this qualification they would be upgraded to grade B. However, it was the view of most managers that an unqualified member of staff would only be a grade B if they could undertake work without having to be supervised. According to the ward manager in the general unit this was clearly not the case with her unqualified nursing staff:

> We made it clear to our grade As that because they are working in a ward environment they are supervised all the time which means they do not warrant being on a grade B pay scale.

Similarly, the senior nurse within the mental health specialty explained that:

> A grade B nurse is one that carries out basic tasks independently of supervision. For example she can take a group of patients out for a shopping expedition for the day or carry out a study session without extensive supervision from the ward manager.

Summary and conclusion

In their respective policy documents, all six of the employers stressed the importance of being able to provide training opportunities to nursing staff that were of relevance to both the organisation and the individual nurse. How were nursing staff expected to apply for such training opportunities? The first method was through a formal application procedure whereby a nurse was expected to fill in a study leave form outlining her request to go on a particular course. This would then be sent to her immediate line manager for approval. If the line manager gave the application her support, it would be forwarded to the senior nurse of the specialty and to personnel for final sanction. The second method was less formal initially in that it involved the ward manager actually approaching a particular nurse and encouraging her to apply for a course. However, the process of application thereafter was the same.

Although the process of application for training opportunities was similar across the six employers, the criteria upon which decisions were made to grant them were very varied. The interviews with managers and an examination of the policy documents showed that four of the employers had no written criteria by which they granted training opportunities. As a result, the criteria upon which managers made such decisions ranged from the subjective, ad hoc and potentially unfair, to the more systematic and formal. A further two employers had policy documents that stated that training opportunities for nursing staff would be identified through individual discussions with nursing staff as part of a regular performance appraisal. As we found out in the preceding chapter, the IPR system of appraisal was not in operation at all in three of the employers, whilst in the remainder it was not operating effectively in relation to staff below the grade of ward manager. Clearly then, the allocation of training opportunities could not be occurring as it was supposed to. The dangers of not having clearly defined criteria upon which decisions were made was illustrated when two ethnic minority nurses felt they were unfairly prevented from going on training courses. Overall, however, it seemed that a lack of training opportunities was a problem facing all staff, irrespective of their ethnicity.

A related issue of central concern was that nursing staff, particularly those below the level of ward manager, were being effectively prevented from taking up training opportunities because of the constraints imposed by an ever decreasing training budget and staff shortages. As a result, employers were increasingly expecting nursing staff to pay for courses themselves and to do them in their own time. Nursing staff were dissatisfied with this, and held that employers ought to be assisting them in the payment of course fees and paid time off, particularly as the organisation and patients would benefit from the resultant improved delivery of care. There was also concern expressed by some nursing staff at the recent organisational changes in the NHS, in particular the move towards trust status and how this had adversely contributed to their opportunities to undertake further training.

There seems little doubt that the criteria by which training opportunities are presently granted are perceived to be unfair and subjective by most nursing staff in our sample, regardless of what occurs in reality. As well as unnecessarily causing harm to employer-employee relations, there is also the danger they could be potentially discriminatory in relation to ethnic minority nursing staff. Two measures could help to address this problem. First, a fully operational appraisal system which systematically identifies the learning needs of each individual nurse needs to be introduced as soon as possible. Secondly, since training opportunities are the key mechanism for further career development, it would be useful, as one employer has done, to begin the process of monitoring training applications by ethnicity. This would go some way in ensuring that the system of granting training opportunities was at least perceived to be fair and equitable by all nursing staff.

6   Equal opportunities

It is often suggested that the NHS has not delivered equality of opportunity to its ethnic minority staff. There is much anecdotal evidence to suggest that despite two decades of anti-discrimination legislation the NHS has been slow to catch up. Partly in order to address this issue the NHS Management Executive set up a programme of action in 1992 which set out to:

> ... ensure that the NHS can secure the staff resources it needs to achieve its goals; that it uses these resources as productively as possible; that staff are properly motivated and treated fairly and responsibly; and that their potential and skill are developed to contribute as fully as possible to the work of the NHS (NHS Management Executive 1993: 4).

One of the key ways in which this strategy is to be achieved is through the drawing up and implementation of equal opportunities policies. An employer's equal opportunities policy should contain a policy statement outlining objectives in key areas such as employment, training and delivery of services. It should also state how the organisation intends to turn the policy into action in these key areas. This is often done in formal codes of practice or more informal guidelines. Both of these should clearly define what is expected or what should be taken into account in undertaking a particular task and who is expected to be responsible. In addition, monitoring is considered a central part of effective equal opportunities policies and is part of the Race Relations Code of Practice (CRE 1994).

This section analyses the equal opportunities policy from six case study employers. We looked at policy documents to investigate their clarity, comprehensiveness and direction. Managers and nursing staff were interviewed to measure the extent of their awareness of the equal opportunities policy and their perceptions of it. We examined the ways in which policy was implemented throughout the organisation. This included whether monitoring information was collected, and to what extent it was analysed and used in the development of action plans. We have documented the level of progress made in turning policy into practice and the degree of faith held in such policies by nursing staff and their managers.

Statement of policy
All of the six employers had adopted formal equal opportunities policies. Most covered broadly the same ground, but in slightly different ways.

- A list of the types of people at risk of discrimination, and an affirmation of action to prevent unfair treatment;

- Reference to legislation (such as the Race Relations Act) and to the roles of statutory bodies (such as the Commission for Racial Equality);

- Details of personnel procedures designed to be fair. Some policies had sections dealing in detail with the three main areas of potential discrimination: race, gender and disability;

- Methods of communicating the policy to staff, potential recruits and others;

- Responsibility for the implementation of the policy identified as resting with general management, line management and staff. Each of these should ensure that they themselves and the next in line was aware of the policy, had received training and adhered to it. Only one employer, however, had appointed a group with specific responsibility for overseeing the equal opportunities policy;

- Collection of information about candidates to enable the policy to be monitored; but few of the policies explained how the data were to be analysed;

- Staff wishing to complain of harassment to be advised to take the matter up informally at first, then formally if not resolved;

- Some policies aimed to spread the policy wider: to contracting organisations and the treatment of patients.

Most employers divided the equal opportunities policy document into a number of sub-sections. Typically these consisted of a code of practice or guidelines on recruitment, selection and promotion, training, grievance, disciplinary and redundancy procedures and pay and conditions of service. A minority were more detailed and contained sections dealing with:

- Equal Pay Act (1970);

- Rehabilitation of Offenders Act (1974);

- Sex Discrimination Act (1975);

- Race Relations Act (1976);

- Disabled Persons (Employment) Act (1994).

A minority of policies indicated a specific review period, typically of two years.

An example policy can be found by looking at employer B. The central aim of this employer's equal opportunities policy was to ensure that employees and job applicants did not receive less favourable treatment on the grounds of age (up to 65), race, religion, colour, nationality, ethnic origin, marital status, gender, disability, sexual orientation, deeply held personal conviction or social and economic class. Reference was made to promotion appropriate to the employee's ability and the employer's needs.

The policy document was divided into three main sections dealing with the Sex Discrimination Act 1975, the Race Relations Act 1976 and the employment of disabled staff. A very brief outline of both the Sex Discrimination Act and the Race Relations Act served to advise on their legal implications. Stereotypical attitudes were highlighted in the policy documents as a barrier to the employment, training, career development and promotion of women. However, no indication was given of how such attitudes might be challenged or changed or what role the employer had in countering stereotypical assumptions amongst its staff and managers. Individual employees were responsible for adhering to the relevant legislation and the employer's equal opportunities policy. Any employee who discriminated on the grounds of sex, race, disability or any other characteristic outlined in the policy or who victimised a complainant was subject to disciplinary action.

The policy of this employer emphasised discrimination against the disabled. The attitudes of non-disabled staff was the starting point for the achievement of equality for disabled staff. By and large it was the attitudes of non-disabled people and their false assumptions about the capabilities of disabled people that hindered recruitment to the workforce. The employer's commitment to the employment of disabled staff was clearly stated. This included a programme of action to make work areas more accessible and the adaptation of equipment to enable disabled people to fill vacancies whenever possible. Line managers were given responsibility to ensure that disabled job applicants were recruited wherever possible and appropriate. Disabled staff would have equality of opportunity in relation to training, career development and promotion.

Taking a slightly different approach, within employer A the equal opportunity policy was set down as a shared responsibility between the personnel department, managers, employees and the Equal Opportunities Group. The Equal Opportunities Group was to be multi-disciplinary in its composition and permanent in its tenure. The remit of this group was initially to develop a monitoring strategy which mapped the progress of the implementation of the equal opportunities policy. Unlike other employers, the pay and conditions of service sub-section dealt with applications for special leave for religious and cultural requirements. This section also made clear that selection criteria for redundancy would be non-discriminatory.

The Sex Discrimination Act, the Race Relations Act, and the 'relevant codes of practice' were referred to briefly under the responsibilities of contractors and others who may carry out work for the employer but are not employed by them. Contractors and others were required to comply with the relevant legislation. It was the responsibility of the personnel department and senior managers to request information on contracted staff to ensure that contractors and others were observing current legislation.

Employer E had the only equal opportunities policy which conferred the same rights to users of the service as to employees. This employer also stated that a much broader range of organisations would be consulted in the implementation of the equal opportunities policy. These included the Commission for Racial Equality, the Equal Opportunities Commission, Whitley Council, the Department of Health and other NHS statutory bodies. Trade unions were given special responsibility in promoting good industrial relations of which equal opportunities were a central part.

Responsibility for communication and implementation

Within most employers, at the policy level, equal opportunities was usually described as a shared responsibility between the personnel department, managers, trade unions and staff associations, employees and in one case, the equal opportunities group. Managers had two primary responsibilities. These included, first, the 'cascade down' or communication of the equal opportunities policy to all employees, and, second, implementing policy directives on a day-to-day basis as they affected selection, recruitment, complaints and grievance procedures. In addition, ward managers were responsible for passing on information about the role and remit of the equal opportunities policy directly to their staff. Individual employees were committed to the policy as a contractual requirement of their employment. By implication non-adherence to this policy could be viewed as a breach of contract.

The communication of the equal opportunities policy was expected to flow from the highest level within the organisation across multiple layers of management to individual members of nursing staff. The way in which this was attempted differed little between employers, with the chief executive and the director of personnel having overall responsibility for the implementation of the policy. In turn, personnel managers were usually responsible for the development and the strategic planning of implementation strategies and line managers putting the policy into practice on a daily basis.

At the highest levels, employers felt that awareness and communication of the equal opportunities policy was the key to its implementation. Personnel department staff, managers and all other employees needed to be made aware of the policy itself and of their responsibilities within it. Awareness was developed in a number of ways, which varied from employer to employer:

- A summary of policy distributed to all employees;

- A summary inserted in the staff handbook;

- Displays on notice-boards;

- Discussions with trade unions, professional associations, joint staff consultative committees and similar forums;

- References to the policy in all recruitment literature;

- Features in the staff newsletter;

- A summary of the policy circulated to job centres, community groups and on-site contractors;

- Equal opportunities training as part of the induction course for new employees.

However, in practice, there were several clear problems with the communication and implementation of the policy. The first was one of acceptance of responsibility. Thus, line managers we spoke to in employers A and B did not see the communication of the equal opportunities policy as part of their role. As one line manager working in the mental health specialty within case study A said, 'I would have thought that [the] personnel [department] would do this'. Indeed, this line manager could not remember ever having seen her employer's equal opportunities policy. Line managers in case study A and B felt the communication of the equal opportunities policy to be the job of the personnel department, the equal opportunities advisor (where one existed) or individual members of nursing staff who should simply seek out the information themselves. Their role as line managers was not to inform but to point out where such information might be available. They did not consider it part of their managerial role to give guidance and advice on the equal opportunities policy and its implications. However, other line managers we spoke to in case study E and F were much more aware of their responsibility in communicating and implementing the equal opportunities policy amongst their nursing staff.

Second, we sometimes encountered a problem of interpretation of the main tenets of the policy. Thus, some line managers in employers C and D reflected a lack of understanding of their employers' equal opportunities statement. For example, one stated:

I'm not sure what an equal opportunity is. I don't care what colour you are as long as you are a good midwife. What's a good equal opportunity? Disabled people can't deliver babies.

It is unlikely that this line manager working within midwifery in case study D would have been able to transmit enthusiasm for her employer's equal opportunities policy to her staff.

Third, it was sometimes the case that the methods for communicating the policy informed new and prospective employees (for example, in case study areas A, B, E and D), but not existing staff. Few employers offered established employees in-house training on equal opportunities issues. Usually personnel officers and managerial staff were the first to benefit from such training. They would, in turn be expected to relay the information and concepts to their own staff. However employer B was developing a customised training programme for different areas of work and levels of staff. It was expected that this would be open to all employees regardless of grade. This was anticipated to run in conjunction with a wider programme to raise the awareness and profile of equal opportunities within the trust. It would seek to explore the employer's legal responsibility in the provision of equality of opportunities and how to deal with harassment.

Channels of communication mentioned mainly concerned new employees. Statement of intent on job advertisements, information given at interviews, induction and when appointed to post formed the bulk of answers given. Few managers interviewed suggested that the current equal opportunities policy was kept on the ward or unit and was therefore available to staff working in these areas. Once employees were established it was unlikely that information on the equal opportunities policy would be communicated to them, unless they were avid notice-board readers. The exception was trade union officials who would use the equal opportunities policy in staff discussions and negotiations.

Few action plans were in progress. Employer B was undertaking a feasibility study which would examine the local ethnic minority community's aspirations and attitudes towards working within the health service. It was expected that any other positive action plans would be based on the findings of this project. Employer E had set up a support group for ethnic minority staff. Its role was to raise staff awareness of the equal opportunities policy. Employer F had set up an Equal Opportunities Committee. The committee was responsible for deciding how best to take the policy forward into action.

Finally, training, a strong theme of all the equal opportunities policy documents, seemed to be rare. Regardless of what we were told by personnel department managers, few managers had been offered training in equalities issues or were aware of any plans to offer them training in the future. Only the most senior managers had been trained on how to implement their employer's equal opportunities policy. Ward managers who were routinely the main agents of recruitment had little if any experience of equal opportunities training.

In general, communication and training addressing the objectives of equal opportunities were limited, leaving both managers and staff confused. Only one employer displayed an active commitment to its equal opportunities policy, in that it was the only employer we came across that not only had action plans but had attempted to put them into practice. Within this employer, recruitment monitoring information was routinely analysed and used to inform policy decisions. Even so, the procedures for collecting monitoring information on training and career development were not in place.

Monitoring

We have seen that all the employers who took part in the research had a written commitment to monitor the implementation of their equal opportunities policy. However, despite this commitment, not all employers were clear which groups or activities would be monitored, or how and when this might start. Most policy documents were vague on specific monitoring details and action plans. In general, policy documents suggested that recruitment and short-listing decisions would be monitored on the basis of ethnicity, sex, disability and marital status and in some cases that employment policies would then be reviewed in the light of monitoring reports produced out of this exercise.

Employer E had recently undertaken a workforce audit. However, most employers were committed to monitoring recruitment rather than workforce activity on the basis of ethnicity, sex, disability and in some cases marital status. Employers E and F collected this information, but did not analyse it:

> We do send out monitoring forms with application forms and [when they are returned] they are kept in a large box under the reception desk. The information should be analysed but is not.

In this case, time and technology were blamed for this state of affairs. There was a commitment to rectify this in the next 12 to 24 months.

Employer A was committed to 'establish a single-minded programme of continuous monitoring to cover a wide range of activity'. In addition, two major projects were planned: the first examined the distribution of ethnic minorities across grades of staff, and the second examined the recruitment and retention of disabled staff. In addition, the Equal Opportunities Group was expected to produce 'periodic' reports, but it was not made clear how often this period might be. Despite such promises we found that monitoring within this employer had started but only gone as far the recruitment process. Information on the ethnicity, gender and disabilities of applicants was routinely collected from application forms. This information was further matched with reasons for or against short-listing for interview. There was some confusion over the analysis of this data with no overall agreement on frequency amongst personnel management. At the time of our research no reports had been produced, but these were anticipated within the following year.

Employer B was the only one which had committed itself to monitoring every stage of the recruitment process. In addition all promotions, training and development opportunities would be monitored. Detailed specifications were included on the monitoring of both internal and external training courses including acceptance and completion rates. Moreover, they would compare differences in the periods of time women, disabled people, black and ethnic minority staff spent in certain grades of work. In practice only recruitment was monitored. Training opportunities, career development and promotion were not monitored. We were not given any indication as to when this additional monitoring was likely to begin.

There was considerable confusion over the extent to which monitoring information was analysed, with personnel managers and other managers giving conflicting suggestions. As a general rule, monitoring reports did not circulate to specialty and line managers.

Perceptions of stated policy

Awareness of an employer's written equal opportunities policy varied greatly. All managers were aware of the policy even if they had not seen it or been given training on how to implement it. Two-thirds of the nursing staff we spoke to were aware of the existence of such a statement or policy. Ethnic minority nursing staff were more likely than their white colleagues not to know whether or not an equal opportunities policy existed, although most staff thought that health service employers probably would or should have such a policy.

Nursing staff who were aware of their employer's equal opportunities policy spoke of the range of ways that it had been communicated to them. Most examples concerned induction material and information given in the course of the recruitment procedure, although not always in a positive fashion. One employee reported that, for instance, 'you're grilled about it at interviews'.

Within some employers, information on the policy and the policy itself had been circulated to wards and seminars had been organised to get the information across. However, in others the staff suggested that information on the equal opportunities policy was sometimes difficult to get:

> They ask a question at interview about what people understand about equal opportunities, but certainly at the time they didn't have an equal opportunities policy that I could get hold of and read because I did ask them for it.

Opinions over whether their employer's equal opportunities policy worked varied, but the many nursing staff reported that they thought it did not. Differences of opinion sometimes varied between specialties, with community staff in particular less aware of and often less confident about equal opportunities policies. This may have been a function of their relative distance and sometimes isolation from the main hospital and administrative base. We also found differences between the reports of members of various ethnic groups. In general white nursing staff were more likely than their ethnic minority colleagues to feel that the equal opportunities policy was a success; one reported that 'we all work together here, we are all given the same opportunities, male, female, black and white'. In contrast, a minority ethnic nurse commented that 'actions speak louder than words, but all I've seen so far are words', and another reported that 'people are either biased or not and a piece of paper stating a policy makes no difference'.

Both white and ethnic minority nursing staff who felt the policy was not working usually based this on a level of cynicism. For example, one commented, 'You know at the end of the day it's only words written on paper', and another said, 'I think it's just a standard thing the hospitals have to have, [It's] just small print'.

Some nursing staff felt that a written equal opportunities policy had simply led to a situation in which discrimination still existed but offenders were more subtle in how this was practised. Amongst ethnic minority staff there was no faith that if procedures were followed the outcome would be fair. In fact it was believed that managers regularly circumvented 'official' procedures:

> It's just talk. It does not make any difference to employment opportunities. [For example] since the recession [her employer] has been employing more white staff and less black staff. You see, now they have a choice, before they did not as all or most applicants would be black.

Recruitment was often given as an example of the policy not working; 'a lot of jobs, yes they advertise them, but they already know who's going to get it. It's a farce'.

Indeed, some ethnic minority nurses were clearly distrustful of the equal opportunities policy; 'it's just a P.R. [public relations] job. There is no real commitment'. Examples were not clearly defined and were more of a feeling:

> I've no proof or experience. Everything is done subtly. You watch the way people handle and speak to certain patients and visitors. Look at the ratio of ethnic minority nurses on the wards. They come in as enrolled nurses and auxiliaries. I don't see them as staff nurses.

These 'feelings' were widely put to us. A written document would be unlikely to change the hearts and minds of staff which would be the real starting point for any change.

The majority of ethnic minority nursing staff we spoke to felt they did not know whether the equal opportunities policy had made a difference. Many of these felt that, regardless of an equal opportunities policy, ethnic minority nursing staff were still often discriminated against:

> All the auxiliaries but one are black and the [only] white auxiliary is going to be the ward clerk. I think the post should have been advertised.

This experience was not unique to unqualified staff:

> There are some overseas nurses being trained here. They are being told that the Health Authority is not offering work permits any more so if they want

work experience they have to get it elsewhere; so I don't think that is equal opportunities.

Few felt the equal opportunities policy made a difference on a day to day basis. However, a small number of ethnic minority nursing staff felt the equal opportunities policy had meant that all staff were treated fairly; 'everyone is given a chance to go for things'.

White nursing staff were much more likely to feel that the equal opportunities policy had made a difference to overall working conditions, one stating, for example, that 'everyone is treated equally here'. The perception of reverse racial discrimination was reported by only one white nurse:

> I don't think there are equal opportunities here. I feel there is favouritism between races. My manager is Mauritian and I think he favours all his Mauritian friends on the unit.

In general the equal opportunities policy alone had generally failed to convince nursing staff that a real commitment was being made. However, for white nursing staff, as long as ethnic minority people were represented on the staff (regardless of the grades they were in), this was 'proof' that the policy must be working:

> I think you can just see it by the employees. You've got the whole spectrum of society here ... it's not just a white, middle-class society.

Some white nursing staff felt the policy was a success in highlighting the damage that having preconceived ideas of particular groups of people could do; 'It just made me aware that while I was interviewing that I must not bias my judgement at all'.

White nursing staff were much more likely to feel that the equal opportunities policy had worked if they themselves had not seen any examples of direct racism:

> I've never seen any problems, I've never really thought about it. To tell the truth it was a big culture shock coming to London. I've never worked with black nurses before.

The issue of equal opportunities was not viewed as a simple black/white division. White nursing staff were more likely to describe equality in gender terms regardless of whether they felt the policy to be working; 'men in nursing get promoted faster than women regardless of qualifications and clinical experience'. In fact, gender was spoken of as frequently as 'race' by white nursing staff; 'it lays down guidelines so that people are more fairly treated, between the sexes and people of different races'. Or 'in ancient times it was the men who got the promotions. Now the women can do just as well'. Disability was also perceived as an equal opportunities issue by some staff:

> What does equal opportunities mean? People just think black and white and that's it ... [but] it can be anything, male, female, colour, deafness, anything.

White nursing staff were more likely to see the failure of the policy as a gender rather than a 'race' issue; 'no the policy is not working. We have still got all the men at the top and all the women at the bottom'. More unusually, one ethnic minority nurse spontaneously referred to gender issues as confirmation of equality of opportunity; 'having a male midwife could be a result of the [equal opportunities] policy'.

Ethnic minority nursing staff were less likely than their white counterparts to feel they had been given equal opportunities; 'some staff are groomed for management jobs. Look around. They are not black'. For ethnic minority staff the issue was clearly one of representativeness:

> At lower levels up to F grade [the representation of black and ethnic minority staff] it is fine, but at the level where influence and decisions are made it does not seem to apply very much. From G onwards I have my doubts.

Ethnic minority staff had little confidence in any equal opportunities policy if senior posts did not reflect the ethnic composition of the workforce overall:

> At senior levels there is only one black person in midwifery. Equal opportunities are not making a difference at the highest levels ... It's only at the lower levels that the local ethnic mix is reflected.

> You won't find one black nursing officer at H or above.

> Not in management, in 10 years I have not seen any black or ethnic minority managers in care of the elderly.

By and large, ethnic minority staff felt they were discriminated against in recruitment and promotional opportunities. This feeling had not changed with the advent of a written equal opportunities policy. Levels of dissatisfaction were higher amongst unqualified and ethnic minority staff who did not feel they had been given equality of opportunity. Some unqualified staff felt that the equal opportunities policy did not apply to them; one said 'equal opportunities? That's for nurses. We can't go on their courses or do their jobs, can we'? while another commented that 'all auxiliaries are given the same opportunity. That's no opportunity'. For auxiliaries there was a general feeling that there were no opportunities for them but that this lack of opportunity was equally applied to all.

Employers had clearly not convinced all of their staff that policies had been put into practice or even what this would mean. Some members of both the white and ethnic minority nursing staff had confused equality of outcome with equality of opportunity. The representation of women or ethnic minority employees at the top of the workforce was felt not to reflect their proportions across the workforce as a whole. They had assumed that equality of outcome would prove or disprove equality of opportunity. Some nursing staff did not understand the concept of the equal opportunities policy. Many thought its objective was to ensure an appropriate number of women and minority groups at the highest levels of the organisation, rather than the removal of discriminatory barriers in the procedures of the organisation.

Summary and conclusion

Managers and their workforce had not been trained and displayed little insight into the policy and their role within it. Unqualified staff frequently did not understand the basis of the policy and equated it with access to further vocational training. Ethnic minority nursing staff were more likely than their white counterparts to display a general distrust and suspicion of the motives behind their employer's equal opportunities policy.

Most nursing staff across our six employers were aware of the existence of their employers equal opportunities policy. This had most often been communicated in the recruitment literature and contracts of employment. However most nursing staff, both ethnic minority and white, felt the policy was not working.

Equality of opportunity clearly had different meanings for white and ethnic minority nursing staff. For some white staff it acted to raise awareness of discrimination not only on the basis of ethnicity but of sex and disability as well. Often for white nursing staff the equal opportunities policy was a promise of equality with men. Until gender equality was achieved the equal opportunities policy had not completed its work. The employment of male auxiliaries was considered 'proof' within one employer that policies did indeed make a difference.

For nursing staff in our study, equal opportunity was largely a statement of intent and not an operational policy.

In the light of our findings it is probably not surprising that much of the nursing workforce was unconvinced of their employer's commitment to equal opportunities. It was widely felt that ethnic minorities were under-represented in senior positions within nursing management. For some ethnic minority staff this was confirmation that opportunities were not equally distributed to all. Equality of opportunity represented tangible outcomes in the representation of staff at higher grades and amongst management. It was not perceived as an absence of discriminatory criteria in organisational procedures and decisions. Nursing staff and in some cases managers had misconstrued equality of opportunity as equality of outcome. Indeed, many thought that equality of outcome either proved or disproved equality of opportunity. The assumption was that one would lead to the other. This had led many staff to become cynical about equal opportunities policies. These were often perceived as solely paper promises. Jewson and Mason (1984) documented similar findings in their study of equal opportunities policies. We found that on occasions this cynicism was well founded. A minority of managers did not consistently follow official policies and procedures.

Most of our employers' equal opportunities strategies broke down in one or more of the following areas:

• The communication of the equal opportunities policy and its application on a daily basis;

• The analysis of any monitoring information;

• The development of action plans.

The communication of the equal opportunities policy was often restricted to recruitment literature and induction information received by new employees. Established employees, including management, were not always aware of their responsibilities in implementing the policy. By and large, employers had failed to communicate effectively the policy and its objectives. Training for managers was patchy and almost non-existent for the nursing workforce.

Despite the Commission for Racial Equality's Code of Practice in employment, only a single employer had completed a workforce ethnic monitoring audit. However, all of our employers routinely monitored recruitment practice. This information was largely not analysed or only analysed on an occasional, ad hoc or irregular basis. Indeed, managers often thought the reason for the collection of ethnic monitoring information was for reference only, in case of an allegation of discrimination in appointing a job candidate. None of the employers monitored promotion or training opportunities even when a commitment to do so was stated in their policy documents. Monitoring is central to the CRE's Race Relations Code of Practice in employment. Without analysing monitoring information it is difficult, if not impossible, to determine any possible inequalities, and their extent. Analysis of monitoring information allows for the effective development of action plans and for the evaluation of those programmes in practice. Although codes of practice are not legally binding, failure to comply with them has been used as evidence of unlawful discrimination at industrial tribunals. Monitoring should be a continuous exercise from the collection of information, analysis of data, compilation of reports, and the use of these reports in action or policy planning. The health service has a particular responsibility to monitor, not only at the recruitment stage, but the entire workforce, and promotion and training opportunities too. As well as identifying possible problems which can inform business planning to avoid possible legal sanction, monitoring can contribute to a positive, professional corporate image in which the talents and potential of all members of the workforce are utilised (see Jewson et al 1992 for a fuller discussion on the merits and benefits of monitoring).

The final report of the Kings Fund Equal Opportunities Task Force (Ellis 1990), set up by the Department of Health, highlighted the point that although most nurse employers had formal equal opportunities policies, few had translated them into a timetabled plan of action or allocated responsibility or resources for achieving such change. With little exception, our findings were very similar. Only one action plan was in operation. Employers still had intentions rather than actions. Training for managers and staff was often only in evidence within the policy documents themselves. Equal opportunities policies will be ineffective without a training programme that seeks to communicate the policy, raise awareness of equal opportunities issues in the workplace and help staff to work in anti-racist ways. The Commission for Racial Equality has outlined the importance of race-related training as part of an equal opportunities policy (for more information see CRE 1989). Ambitious plans to collaborate with other agencies and statutory bodies had not emerged. Our findings are similar to those of Iganski (1992). His survey of equal opportunities in Health Authorities found only a minority who were putting policy into practice. Jewson et al (1992), also produced a review of employers considered to be 'advanced' in their monitoring activities. Amongst these 'advanced' employers it was found that most were in developmental stages with regards to data collection and analysis and had not set up action plans or policies to respond to the results of the monitoring exercise. Some of the monitoring plans of our case study employers were extremely ambitious and it was not surprising to find they had not been implemented.

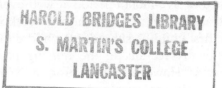
7 Flexible working arrangements and child care

The NHS must set the pace in the 1990s as the best employer of women. This is not 'positive discrimination' but 'enlightened self interest'... it needs to recruit, retrain and provide the best career opportunities for women at all levels in the NHS. It must not be 'as good as' but better than other employers at providing imaginative and flexible arrangements to enable women to combine work and family responsibilities (Virginia Bottomley, Secretary of State for Health, May 1991, cited in NUPE 1992: 3).

According to Labour Force Survey data, women now comprise almost 50 per cent of the total national workforce (Jones 1993). Further, they also comprise over 90 per cent of the nursing workforce (Department of Health 1994). However, despite such relatively high levels of economic activity there is little evidence to suggest that their overall responsibility for family and domestic arrangements are changing to take account of their increased representation in the labour market. Working parents, particularly working mothers, are often faced with difficult problems such as finding and affording child care facilities. It is known that there are variations in rates of economic activity between women from different ethnic groups (Jones 1993). In addition, we know that some ethnic groups have larger families or are more likely to be single parents than white women. Lack of child care and flexible working opportunities may disproportionately discriminate against some ethnic minority groups.

The postal survey of nursing staff suggests the percentage of working women with dependent children is approximately the same for both white and black women (see Chapter 9, Table 9.3). However, black women are more likely to work shifts, and work for longer hours, often reflected in more than one paid job, than white women. It is possible that black nurses with dependent children are more likely to be disadvantaged by inflexible child care.

A study of nearly 8,000 nurses conducted in 1988 found that pregnancy was the most common reason nurses gave for leaving their jobs (Price Waterhouse 1988). The NHS Women's Unit calculated the cost for a single trust to replace and retrain all those women who had left its employment in a twelve-month period at well over a million pounds a year (Alimo-Metcalfe 1993). A low return to work rate for nurses after the birth of their first child or subsequent children is a costly waste of resources. Traditionally recruits to the nursing profession came from female school leavers. However, a reduction in the numbers of suitably qualified school leavers and increased competition for them from other employers has compelled the NHS to examine alternative strategies. Emphasis has shifted to a reduction in turnover and wastage and to the recruitment and retention of women with children.

In order to address these issues the NHS Management Executive and the Department of Health stated their commitment to raising 'the profile of issues relating to the work of women within the NHS, and to accelerate the slow progress that has already taken place in providing equal opportunities for women' (cited in Goss & Brown 1991: 4).

Employers' provision of child care can take a number of forms workplace nurseries, places at other local nurseries, child care vouchers and holiday play-schemes. A survey carried out in 1991 of nearly 5,000 women going back to work after having a baby found that 50 per cent wanted improved child care facilities. Indeed, most had a preference for workplace child care (McRae 1991). However, only 60 of 279 health-care employers in a recent survey had workplace nurseries (Labour Research Department 1992: 20).

Flexible working arrangements give employees more choice over the hours and the way they work. They can enable staff with child care responsibilities to continue a career in the NHS; they can open up career opportunities for part-time work in management and senior posts which would usually only be available to full-time employees. They can provide better conditions of service and can be used as part of a recruitment and retention strategy. Flexible child care and working arrangements lessen the possibilities for indirect discrimination against those who are unable or unwilling to work set, rigid hours or full-time hours.

Chapters 9 and 10 contain detailed information from the postal survey of nursing staff on working patterns and flexible working arrangements. The findings of the survey showed:

- ethnic minority nursing staff were much more likely to be working full-time than their white colleagues. Over half of white nursing staff were working part-time;

- over half of the nursing and midwifery staff were working on a rotating shift basis;

- over half of nursing staff in all ethnic groups had taken at least one career break;

- the most common reason for taking a career break was to deal with child care responsibilities.

In this chapter, based on in-depth interviews with nursing and midwifery staff, a number of questions are addressed, including:

- the extent to which employers had formal policies covering flexible working arrangements and child care;

- the extent to which nursing staff made use of these opportunities and the overall level of satisfaction nursing staff felt towards the level of provision provided by their employers;

- any difficulties or barriers faced by nursing staff in taking up child care provisions or flexible working opportunities.

It should be noted that any member of nursing staff to whom the lack of flexible working arrangements had proved an impenetrable obstacle would not be interviewed as they would have left their employment.

Statement of policy

Flexible working arrangements were sometimes discussed as part of an employer's equal opportunities policy. Career breaks, part-time working, job sharing and child care provision were examined under the heading of flexible working. Most employers had a range of flexible working arrangements and in all but employer C these were agreed and accepted management policy. There was some variation from employer to employer but written policy always included:

- Career breaks. Time off to care for a dependent, usually to look after a child, or more rarely for personal study;

- Job share. The dividing of one post (usually full-time) into two posts, with pro rata salary and benefits.

And in most employers:

- Part-time working. Turning a full-time post into a part-time post.

Most employers operated a qualifying period, typically one year, which employees would have to satisfy before becoming eligible for any of the above schemes.

Job share

Job share enables two people to share the salary, hours, duties and responsibilities of one full-time job. In most job shares, two people divide up the hours and are paid salary and other benefits pro rata. Job sharing is often confused with part-time work. However, job sharing differs from part-time work in that it is a single full-time post shared by two employees, not two separate part-time posts. In a part-time post the hours are usually decided by management, whereas job sharers themselves decide how to share part of a full time job.

Job sharing offers a number of advantages to employers:

• Reduction in staff turnover;

• Greater flexibility of staffing;

• Availability of a wider range of skills than can be provided by one full-timer;

• The possibility of employing appropriate staff who are unwilling or unable to work full-time.

The disadvantages of job sharing are few but include increased training and administration costs and possibly increased time for communication and supervision.

Amongst most of our six employers, all posts were potentially eligible for job share. Full-time employees could request to share their post. In some cases this included women already on maternity leave. Job share was not available to night staff within employer B. However, night staff could work on a part-time basis with a two night minimum.

Line managers were given the responsibility of deciding the practicability of job sharing any particular post. If agreed, action was taken within a set period, typically three months. Existing employees usually had to continue working full-time until a job sharer was found. When a request for job sharing was refused or attempts to find a sharer were unsuccessful, further applications involving the same post were often not permitted for a set period, typically up to twelve months. Employers varied in their response to cases where a job sharing partner could not be found. Within some, employees were not compelled to continue to work full-time, but with others they were. Other strategies would often be explored including the re-allocation of duties, redeployment and the creation of a part-time post.

Flexitime

This allows employees to work their contracted hours within a range of times. The working day is usually divided up into core and flexible hours. Employees must be in attendance during core hours, for instance between 10am and 2pm. The remainder of the employee's contracted hours can be worked in a variety of ways. Adjustments can be made on a daily, weekly or monthly basis. In some cases an extra day's leave can be acquired over a period. This system allows employees to adjust their working hours to suit other commitments even at quite short notice.

Case studies A, B and C offered flexible working hours in which the work time was divided up into core and flexible hours. Certain periods throughout the day were considered 'high demand periods' and all staff were expected to be on duty. Other segments of the day were defined as 'low demand periods'. Staff were given a level of flexibility over which 'low demand periods' they wished to work. Employers B and C suggested that flexible full-time working hours were not possible for staff working in clinical areas, and therefore restricted them to administrative posts.

Term time only working

Term time only working allows employees to work solely during school term times and not during holidays. This allows parents with child care responsibilities to continue their careers without having to take lengthy breaks. It gives them continuity of employment and employment rights.

Only employers A and B offered school term-time only contracts.

Career breaks

These allow employees, usually women, to leave work, in some cases for up to five years, to deal with child care responsibilities. Some employers allow employees to use career breaks for periods of extended study. Employees are usually entitled to the same grade of job on their return. These schemes do not 'cost' the employer in terms of pay or continuing contributions as the employee is not in their employment in this period. However, there are costs associated with up-dating or retraining at the point of re-entry.

A career break scheme in one form or another was operated by all six employers. It allowed employees to have a period of one to five years away from work without pay. The purpose of career break schemes was on the whole 'to enable staff to spend more time with their families'. Applications were made directly to the line manager who in conjunction with the personnel department considered applicants' requests. Employe

F suggested that selection criteria such as 'satisfactory performance,' should be taken into account when deciding whether to allow a career break. Employer F also expected staff on career breaks to work on an ad hoc basis for a minimum of 75 hours a year. This would constitute one way of maintaining skills and knowledge over the career break period. Some employers operated a re-entry programme to facilitate a return to work for those ending a career break. This usually took the form of joint responsibility between employer and employee. The employer provided opportunities for training and up-dating to employees on career breaks; and employees on career breaks undertook to keep up to date with professional and departmental developments. On return to work the employee's post or an equivalent would be made available to them.

If a career break was not possible, managers usually considered other options such as:

- Part-time working;

- Job share;

- Flexible working hours;

- School term-time only contracts.

Short-term leave

Many women find it difficult to combine employment with responsibility for children or other dependent relatives, because of the need to take time off at short notice to deal with sickness or other crises. Employers may offer special arrangements to allow leave on such occasions. Short-term leave may be disruptive to work schedules, but formal arrangements may be better than ad hoc release on 'sick leave'. Arrangements for special leave may allow many women to continue nursing when they would otherwise have left the profession. Special leave can take a range of forms, for example, time off for urgent domestic distress, parenthood leave, time off to look after sick relatives and time off for religious and cultural observances. Short-term leave can remove a possible source of indirect discrimination against women and ethnic minority staff.

Flexible working in practice

Management

On the whole, most senior personnel and line managers were aware of the range of flexible working arrangements and had a real commitment towards enabling nursing staff to work the hours that best fitted in with their outside or domestic obligations. A line manager from case study C explained that 'we try not to be rigid with hours of work, we try to accommodate say 9am 3pm for staff with child care problems'.

Although there was a broad commitment to flexible working arrangements amongst most employers, this was clearly within the confines of the service. Career breaks and job shares were encouraged by management wherever possible but, 'we have to meet the needs of the service as well as the needs of the nurse, there has to be flexibility on both sides'.

Managers at all levels echoed this sentiment of a fine balance being struck between employees and service needs. 'We try to incorporate these [job share, career break, part-time working] desires, but patient care must always come first.'

Managers were concerned that flexible working arrangements might adversely affect service provision and should be organised around the efficiency of the service at all times. A line manager from case study D stated that 'flexible working arrangements have to meet and fit in with the needs of the service, first and foremost'.

Job sharing for nursing staff was popular with line managers in case study E. It was considered particularly important for nurses at ward sister or charge nurse level:

> Job share is open to all whether you have a [job share] partner or not. This is particularly important for nurses at grade G and above who want to work part-time but part-time posts are not at G grade.

However, it was clear that policies on flexible working arrangements had not filtered down to all line managers, with a number in employers B, C and D unaware of some or all of them, as this senior nurse in employer C stated, 'there are no job shares or flexible working arrangements for nursing staff in this hospital'.

A small number of line managers in employer B were largely operating informal agreements amongst staff. One manager told us that posts cannot be held open for career break staff nor could equivalent posts be guaranteed on their return. Indeed one director of nursing services stated that job sharing was not 'allowed for nurses' and this was open to management staff only. However, she would 'try' and be flexible with hours of work. This director was not aware of her employer's career break policy and suggested that any leave of this type would be an informal arrangement up to a maximum of six months.

Overall, amongst all employers, the actual numbers of nursing staff participating in the job sharing scheme was low, as this personnel department representative in employer E informed us:

> I think the problem is not many staff are interested or if they are it is difficult to find someone else to do the other part of the post. It does not work very well and there is not much up-take of job share.

The personnel department in employer E preferred part-time to job sharing arrangements:

> One of the best ways to be flexible is through part-time working. That works well and managers don't have a stereotype about having to be full-time to be a 'proper' member of staff.

Part-time posts in employer E, when offered, were often only at lower grades. Nurses returning to the workforce on a part-time basis might have to risk their career development:

> Managers are happy for people to work less hours but people have to be able to cover their shifts and not everyone can go on a 9am - 5pm or nights. In fact we have a lot of [maternity leave] returners on nights but we are trying not to have purely night [only] staff as they do not get up-dated like other staff do.

The NHS used to offer contracts of employment which allowed nursing staff to work solely on nights or solely on days rather than rotating between days and nights. These contracts were popular with nursing staff with caring responsibilities. Such contracts benefited individual employees who knew exactly when they would be working, and could plan accordingly, but are now viewed as detrimental by all the employers we spoke to:

> We do not say to staff 'you have children, you can work flexitime'. We have had problems in the past with staff working specific nights which have caused problems for other members of staff and problems in service provision. It's very difficult. On the one hand you should be encouraging people to work the hours they can. Then you have got the other side, the management side where this causes a problem because you have staff that have to work round them and problems with study leave and holidays.

Personnel management in employer C confirmed that day or night only contracts were no longer being offered. The emphasis was now on flexibility for the employer rather than the employee:

> Flexible working patterns are being implemented ... they are moving away from day or night only contracts. Rotation working is being implemented. If staff have individual needs and circumstances these will be taken into account only if they can be fitted into the overall implementation of service and staff needs.

Staff

Most nursing staff were aware of some but not all of the possible flexible working arrangements offered by their employer. Part-time working was the most widely known amongst staff. However, there was much less awareness of career breaks, and job sharing was sometimes seen as one of the advantages of working in the community. ' Job share is available in the community but I have not come across it in the hospital.'

Few staff with children throughout our six employers had used such schemes, in particular flexible full-time and part-time hours. However, nursing staff did not always see flexible working arrangements in a positive light:

> Special/flexible shift working is a burden rather than a benefit. You have got an obligation to get the work done [in fewer hours] because they [the management] are doing you a favour.

There was some concern that an increase in flexibility would mean a decrease in salary. 'If it meant being paid less I couldn't do it, but I would like more flexible hours.'

Some staff had never considered working more flexible or fewer hours and others thought the financial limitations of living on a part-time wage made it inconceivable. Difficulties were highlighted:

> There was not any part-time available when I wanted to do it. I didn't go into job sharing. To be honest I didn't know much about it and nor did my manager. Who would I share with? It was finding a partner, there was nobody to share with.

A minority of nursing staff had used part-time and job share arrangements. In employer E many of the nursing staff we spoke to had utilised such arrangements: 'the authority has not been a problem. I have chosen the hours I want to work'.

Working part-time and nights only were still popular with nursing staff. In the past staff had often used one or the other as a way of juggling work and caring responsibilities. However, nursing staff felt that working hours had generally become more rigid and less flexible in recent years. As one nurse said, 'there seems to be less flexibility. All contracts are now internal rotation, there are no more nights only for parents'.

One nurse thought that working days or nights only would be detrimental to her career:

> I don't think I could [do days or nights only] without losing my grade. In this grade we must do days and nights and not go off sick too much. They really watch you closely these days.

This was not the only nurse who suggested that flexibility in working hours was a function of certain grades and would not apply to F grades and above, that is, ward managers and first line nursing management.

Child care

All of our six employers had a written child care policy. Employers A and D were looking at the possibility of introducing child care vouchers for employees. Child care vouchers are particularly attractive as they can be used to pay for all legally permissible child care providers, including members of the family. These vouchers would not cover the whole cost of child care but typically a third to half of the total cost was indicated. It was noted that to introduce such a scheme for all employees would be expensive. The working party set up by employer A to look into this issue suggested the use of such a scheme for particular posts or types of staff if recruitment and retention became particularly difficult. Such an offer would be withdrawn if and when recruitment and retention no longer posed a problem.

Child care in practice

Five employers operated an on-site nursery or a creche and employer A had access to places at a locally run facility. Somewhat surprisingly senior management in employer A suggested that few of their nursing staff had young children. This was the main reason given for collaborating in an 'outside' scheme rather than setting up an in-house, workplace nursery.

The opening and closing of these provisions broadly mirrored office hours. All opened five days a week, Monday to Friday. They did not operate over week-ends and bank holidays. In case study B subsidised rates for single parents were offered while case studies C and D offered child care provisions for school holidays such as summer play-schemes.

A significant proportion of nursing staff with children we interviewed across all employers were not aware of any child care facilities provided by their employer, although many suggested they would consider using such a facility if they knew of its existence. Very few of the nursing staff we interviewed had used employer child care facilities. The price and the incompatibility of opening hours were the main obstacles expressed by nursing staff. Nursery or creche opening hours were clearly incompatible with the working hours of most nursing staff which reflected a 24 hour rota. 'It's a nursery but midwives tend to make alternative arrangements because the opening hours don't fit in with their shift patterns.'

However, many nursing staff, although recognising that employer child care facilities were expensive and not always fitting in with the demands of shift-work, would have liked the opportunity to use such a facility but were unable to secure a place because of high demand. For some nursing staff the problem was one of over-subscription: '[The nursery] costs about £80 per week and has a long waiting list. Nurses have to put their name down when they are pregnant and hope to get a place.'

Some nursing staff felt employer child care facilities were designed for administrative or secretarial staff rather than nursing staff:

> ... [the nursery] is for the whole hospital and competition for places is high. The nursery is expensive and tends to be used by secretarial staff more than nursing and midwifery staff.

Or

> We have got a nursery here which is very expensive. It's mainly nursing officers' and doctors' children that are there. I don't think any of the plebs like me can afford it. Yes, we have got a nursery, but it is open from 7am, that's fine if we start at 7.30am, but it closes at 6pm. So, if you are on a late, which means you start at 1pm or 2pm, it means that hubby or nanny or somebody has got to get to the nursery to pick up the child because it's not open when your shift finishes. It's not open bank holidays and it's not open week-ends, and it costs fifteen pounds a day.

One nurse went further by suggesting that the nursery was purposely not designed for use by nursing or unqualified staff:

> The only people who use the nursery here are the well-paid consultants cum doctors. It's un-affordable to people who are on basic salaries such as porters, ancillary workers, auxiliary nurses ... mostly they don't get a look in. They are not even considered, I think they're considered as non-people.

Some line managers considered the waiting list to be unreasonably long:

> The hospital provides a nursery but places are incredibly tight. You have to put your name down six months before you have a baby.

Most levels of management we spoke to in nearly all employers were aware that nursery/creche and holiday play-schemes, where they existed, were heavily over-subscribed. One manager clearly thought this had affected the recruitment and retention of mothers with dependent children:

> Both are heavily over-subscribed ... it's not enough to meet our needs. There is no question that a lot of women are deterred from working as a result of our child care arrangements.

As a result of the demand on places, an informal allocation scheme was in operation within employer D, as this personnel manager informed us:

> ... [the nursery] has very few spaces. The facility is there and people are encouraged to use it. It [the allocation] is designed on the basis that those that

have the most important jobs in the organisation are the ones that get allocated places first. It is done on a hierarchal basis.

When probed on the meaning of 'most important' we were told: 'It's to do with your standing and status in the organisation. They have to discriminate and this is what they do'.

Limited places had made competition fierce. In addition, line managers generally recognised that opening hours did not fit in with nursing staff's shift patterns. This comment was typical of those we were given by line managers:

> Most nurses are aware of the creche but feel it does not suit them. It does not open until 7.30am, so it's no good for nurses on the early shift. It shuts at 5.30pm, so it's no good for nurses on the late shift. It's very much for people who work 9am - 5pm. It does not cater for nursing staff but other staff, like Human Resources for instance.

This had a knock-on effect on staffing patterns:

> If they are doing night duty [or] weekends there is no [child care] facility run by the hospital to cater for this. They just have to make outside arrangements and that's when difficulties on the ward start.

Senior managers generally recognised that staff child care needs were not being dealt with in terms of accessibility, price or time. Some facilities did not take babies under a year old, all had long waiting lists, opening hours did not reflect shift patterns and at a minimum of £75 per week, were expensive in relation to the pay levels of the bulk of nursing staff. However despite widespread problems, discussions for expanding child care facilities for all grades of nursing staff were only taking place within employer D.

These examples were typical of the experiences of nursing staff in their attempts to organise appropriate child care. Nursing staff clearly desired a workplace child care facility that was accessible, affordable and fitted in with their working hours. Unfortunately, they perceived the current facilities available as offering none of these advantages. On site child care facilities were seen by some nursing and managerial staff as the preserve of the 'well-paid'. Nurses did not see themselves as a part of this group, and, more important, they were not seen as such by their managers.

Summary and conclusion
Although the possibility of job-sharing was available, actually finding a person to job share with was rather more difficult. Flexible working mainly consisted of nursing staff using formal or informal arrangements

of doing nights or days only or taking short periods of unpaid leave when faced with particular domestic responsibilities. However, all these arrangements were dependent upon the smooth running of the service delivery.

Some senior managers interviewed suggested a level of apprehension from staff, as well as management, with regard to flexible working arrangements. Job sharing in particular was felt to be difficult to implement and to have a negative impact on service delivery. A minority thought that the 24 hour shift working rota was 'part of the job' and that staff should simply 'get used to it'. Good practice had not been communicated to all managers and significant numbers of nursing staff were both unclear or unaware of the level and range of flexibility offered by their employer. The decline of part-time and night only shifts, without the widespread communication of alternative job sharing and career break options, has made nursing staff think working conditions have become less inflexible. Some staff would have liked the opportunity to work reduced hours, job share or a career break but there was widespread concern of the financial and career penalties this might incur.

Part-time work and working nights only were widely utilised by nursing staff and part-time working was generally encouraged by management as part of flexible working arrangements. However, part-timers and staff working solely nights did not feel they were given the same access to career and training developments as their full-time colleagues. A survey carried out in 1993 found that 40 per cent of part-timers and 41 per cent of night-only staff had spent any time on training in the last twelve months compared to 25 per cent of people working full-time (Jackson & Barber 1993). It was widely recognised that there are currently few career opportunities available to those who work part-time or nights only. It is important to ensure where staff are working on special shifts or part-time that they are given equal opportunities to training and career development as their full-time or rotation counterparts.

Workplace nurseries are the child care preference of most parents. Parent and child can travel in to work and back home together, and are near enough to have regular day-time contact. In addition, parents are close at hand in the event of illness or an emergency. However, hospitals are often spread over a number of sites, only one of which is likely to offer nursery provisions. All of our participating employers offered nursing staff child care facilities on a sole site. With a single exception, these were typically workplace creches or nurseries. These were offered on a 'first come first served' basis, or on rarer occasions priority was given to certain job holders, usually to senior or managerial posts considered difficult to recruit. In operation, both systems meant there was little link between those with child care places and those with the greatest child care needs. Nursery opening hours did not reflect the shift system worked by the vast majority of nursing staff. A recent survey reported that over 70 per cent of nursing staff work on the week-ends (Jackson & Barber 1993). None of these child care provisions offered by employers opened 'late night' or at the week-ends. These facilities were certainly not 'nurse-friendly'. Jackson & Barber (1993) found that 52 per cent of nurses and midwives in their sample had found it difficult to get the amount of child care they would like.

The interviews carried out in this study clearly showed that women were dissatisfied with the child care facilities offered by their employers because they were out of the price range of all but the most senior nurses. Amongst the employers who took part in the case studies we found the price of a full-time nursery or creche place was in the region of £70 - £85 per week. As the average gross annual salary of an E grade nurse is in the region of £13,500 (Review Body for Nursing Staff, Midwives, Health Visitors and Professions Allied to Medicine 1994) or just under £260 per week, these fees are clearly unrealistic.

It should be borne in mind that these problems are not unique to nursing staff. There is recent evidence to suggest that the cost of child care is growing faster than the rate of wage inflation (Finlayson et al. 1995). Furthermore, Marsh & McKay (1993) found that women who paid for child care typically spent 25 per cent of their earnings on it. At this time none of these employers offered child care vouchers or child care allowances. Waged work largely continues not to accommodate the needs of women's caring responsibilities.

It is clear that increased flexibility is needed in terms of operating times, price and types of child care offered. Child care allowances could provide for more flexibility as employees could use allowances to pay for private child care of their own choice. This would give employees far greater control over their child care requirements. It would enable them to choose who looked after their child(ren), in a place suitable for the needs of both parent(s) and child(ren). Eligibility for child care allowances could be set at low salary levels, or restricted to certain categories to ensure some link between allowance allocation and need.

The absence of proper child care provisions and inflexible structures for work and careers are two of the barriers to equality highlighted by the Hansard Society Commission (cited in Goss and Brown 1991). Career level posts are often seen to be full-time posts only which reinforces the lack of training opportunities for part-timers. Lack of adequate child care provision makes it difficult for women to 'juggle' the joint responsibilities of family and career and can have the effect of creating an artificial brake on career escalation. Goss and Brown (1991) describe how these barriers operate against women in the NHS. In particular, shift working and a lack of flexible working and child care arrangements can have the effect of 'trapping' some women in posts which do not reflect their skills, experience or potential.

8 Relationships with patients and colleagues

Racial discrimination in the workplace is used to refer to the forms of unfair treatment people are subjected to in relation to access to jobs, training and promotion (Home Office 1977). These forms of workplace discrimination have been covered in the preceding chapters. However, it can also include a particular form of unfair treatment, racial harassment, and it is this element that is the subject of this chapter. Since the early 1980s, many employers, particularly those in the public sector, have adopted equal opportunities policies declaring their opposition to racial harassment and providing a grievance procedure to address any cases that may arise.

The 1988 British Crime Survey (BCS) obtained a partial measure of the extent of racial abuse at work. Respondents were asked whether they had been subjected to verbal abuse from someone they came into contact with in their job, other than a colleague, in the past fourteen months.[1]

Table 8.1 shows that one in seven members of all ethnic groups had been verbally abused at least once over the period of just over a year. Approximately half of the Asians and black people who had been verbally abused stated there had been a racial dimension to the insult. It should be noted that the survey did not examine racial harassment from colleagues at work and therefore represents only a partial picture (Aye Maung and Mirrlees-Black 1994).

Assessing levels of racial harassment is difficult. 'Low level' racial harassment in the form of racial abuse and other forms of insulting behaviour are often excluded from existing studies, despite the

---

1   The British Crime Survey (BCS) is a victimisation survey which sets out to establish a more accurate picture of crime by covering people's experience of victimisation over the last year irrespective of whether they have reported it to the police. This helps to establish what is commonly referred to as the 'dark figure' of crime, that is, the level of unrecorded crime (Mayhew et al 1989: 2). The 1988 BCS comprised a nationally representative 'core' sample of 10,392 households aged 16 or older, and an additional 'booster' sample of 1,349 black people and Asians to allow a more reliable picture of the scale of crime against them.

Table 8.1   Verbal and racial abuse at work: 1988 BCS

Percentages

	White	Black	Asian
Employees subjected to any verbal abuse at work	14	14	16
Those abused, who attributed a racial motive	2	44	56

(table derived from Aye Maung and Mirrlees-Black 1994:10)

potentially damaging nature of such behaviour, particularly if undertaken on a persistent basis against an individual (see Virdee 1995 for a discussion). It is clear that abuse and harassment are not everyday occurrences for many ethnic minority employees. On the other hand, there may be an undercurrent of racial taunts which affect some workers directly and may cause distress to a wider group of people who feel isolated and threatened. The primary responsibility for confronting this problem lies within the workplace with management, trade unions or staff associations, and with the employees themselves.

This chapter comprises three main sections. The first section explores the nature of racial harassment faced by nursing staff from patients. The second section examines the racial harassment experienced by nursing staff from colleagues and the third section looks at the actions taken by nursing staff in addressing the problem, in particular whether they reported the incidents to management and the response of management in dealing with such incidents. The chapter, based on depth interviews with a small number of nurses in each work group, provides a clear indication of the nature of racial harassment, and of what it feels like to be on the receiving end of such behaviour. It does not seek to provide an accurate measure of the extent of the problem but rather explores the nature of the problem, the personal and power relationships between harassed and harasser and the circumstances in which the problem arises.

The findings of the postal survey reported in Chapter 13 provide important complementary information for this qualitative material. The survey showed clearly the extent of the problem of racial harassment, concluding that:

• Members of the ethnic minority groups were consistently more conscious of racial harassment than white nurses were;

- The most common experience was racial abuse or other types of racial harassment by patients or their families: up to two-thirds of ethnic minority nurses reported this;

- More than a third said that they had been racially harassed by work colleagues.

The results discussed below are presented against a background in which racial harassment at work has received considerable attention from employers. All our employers included their opposition to racial harassment at work within their equal opportunities policies. A minority went further and had developed detailed harassment policies.

Racial harassment from patients

Ethnic minority nursing staff in all six case study areas reported having been subjected to racial harassment from patients. However, the problem varied in scale and nature across the different employers and specialties within each employer. Broadly speaking, this racial harassment from patients could be broken down into two distinct forms. First, there was a form of harassment where the racial motivation in the incident was clear because of the accompanying verbal insults or because the patient had made it clear they did not want to be nursed by an ethnic minority nurse. Secondly, there was a more subtle form of racial harassment where white patients did not explicitly mention the nurse's ethnicity but rather treated ethnic minority nurses in a relatively unfavourable way compared to their manners with white nurses.

The study found numerous examples of ethnic minority nursing staff being subjected to forms of racial harassment where the racial motivation was made explicit by the patients. In the midwifery specialty of case study C, half of the ethnic minority midwifery and nursing staff interviewed reported being racially harassed by patients. One ethnic minority nurse recounted an incident where 'a woman said she did not want a black woman to deliver her baby'. Similarly, in another incident, a white senior midwife working alongside an ethnic minority colleague to deliver the baby recalled an incident where the expectant mother 'made it clear she did not want to be looked after by a "black"'.

Racial abuse from patients against ethnic minority nursing staff was widespread across all the employers studied. Ethnic minority nurses working in the community unit of case study A reported that most of the racial harassment they encountered from patients comprised incidents of verbal abuse. Again, within the community unit of case study B, nurses reported being racially abused. In a small number of cases however, the form of racial harassment took on a more violent nature with ethnic minority nurses and midwives recounting incidents of doors being slammed in their faces by white patients. Within the medical specialty of case study D, nearly all the ethnic minority nursing staff recalled incidents of being verbally abused by patients. One ethnic minority nurse reported how 'there was one [patient] who was swearing at everybody, but with me she used racial remarks. I wasn't upset. I just walked away'. Such remarks were not confined to patients who were rude and abusive to all nursing staff irrespective of their ethnicity. Often ethnic minority nurses would be singled out for such treatment by patients who were not abusive to white nursing staff.

Ethnic minority staff perceived some groups of patients as more likely than others to be rude and racially abusive. An ethnic minority nurse working in the community unit in case study E suggested that:

> ... with elderly people it comes out all the time. I don't really take it on board. I have gone to people I know did not really want me because of the way they spoke to me ... sometimes they even talk about 'foreigners' or 'black people' to me.

Similarly, another nurse working with the elderly in case study E recounted a racial incident whereby a white man 'called me a "black so and so"'.

Some white nursing and midwifery staff recognised that they were viewed by white patients in a more favourable way than their ethnic minority colleagues. Furthermore, they acknowledged that their ethnic minority colleagues were regularly subjected to racial harassment by some white patients. Indeed, several white nurses and midwives in our study reported witnessing the racial harassment of ethnic minority nursing staff by white patients. For example, in case study D, a white nurse recounted how she saw an ethnic minority nurse being racially abused by a white patient.

The study found that on some occasions, patients attempted to use white nurses and midwives as a channel to express their reluctance to be treated by ethnic minority staff. A white midwife explained how a white patient had said:

> 'Don't send one of those blacks in. I want a white midwife'. I was really embarrassed and didn't know what to do. I took the senior midwife to one side and she made sure a white midwife looked after that mother.

It should be noted that, although the majority of white nursing staff interviewed were sympathetic to the problem of racial harassment faced by their ethnic minority colleagues, there was a small minority of white staff who felt that such incidents had to be understood in the context of the patient's suffering and hence such incidents should not be construed as being racially motivated. A white midwife recounted an incident where she saw an ethnic minority colleague being called 'racial names', but argued that 'although it would be untruthful to say that the nurses were not being abused... There can be verbal aggression, but it's not really racist, it's just because of their frustration'.

The second type of racial harassment that ethnic minority nursing staff were subjected to from patients comprised those things that were left unsaid and the looks that they were given when they came to 'nurse' particular white patients. As one ethnic minority nurse said, 'sometimes I get the feeling that they would rather not have me'. In such incidents, there was no overt racial abuse from patients but rather a more subtle rejection by them of being cared for by ethnic minority nurses. An ethnic minority nurse working in the medical specialty of case study D described an incident of this type when she stated that 'it's a feeling you get. When a patient asks for somebody else and you feel you are not wanted there'. A midwife working in case study D also reported how this type of racial harassment was often quite subtle in nature. 'It happens quite a lot, quite minor things. Sometimes a patient may show more appreciation to a white nurse than me.' A patient's body language was often perceived as an indication of uneasiness towards an ethnic minority nurse:

> You try to be kind, but you know you can feel it. You know when it's racial.
> If someone is in pain or they have got problems, there is a difference [between
> that and] when someone despises you because of your colour. They give you
> a cold look and you can't reach them.

Another ethnic minority nurse recounted how white patients were often horrified by the thought of being treated by an ethnic minority nurse when she said that 'patients look at me as if I come from outer space because they are expecting a white nurse'.

Further examples of this type of racial harassment against ethnic minority nursing and midwifery staff were found in the other case study areas looked at. A reluctance to ask ethnic minority staff to help and a preference for a white nurse were common. Within the elderly specialty of case study E, some staff reported that a patient's body language, tone of voice or avoidance of eye contact often suggested that they were uncomfortable being nursed by ethnic minority nurses. 'You can see from some of the patients. They tend not to come too close or not to want you to help them because of your colour.' Alternatively, patients sometimes complained unfairly to their family or white nursing staff about their treatment by ethnic minority nursing staff.

Although most of the racial harassment was of a non-violent nature, the study did find that some nursing staff working in the community felt vulnerable to attack while visiting patients in their own homes. In the case of ethnic minority nurses this risk took on an added racial dimension. Some nursing staff reported that patients were less likely to be constrained by any notion of 'good manners' or 'acceptable behaviour' than they might have been within a ward or clinic situation. Patients were more likely to be 'open' about their racism within their own homes.

In addition to relating such incidents of racial harassment, ethnic minority nursing and midwifery staff suggested possible explanations for their patients' behaviour. In the midwifery specialty in case study B, racial harassment by patients was often rationalised by the ethnic minority midwives interviewed as being an 'expression of the pain' the patients were suffering. For example, a minority midwife recounted an incident where a white patient had said 'don't touch me you black cow. But I know she didn't mean it. It was a difficult delivery and she was having a hard time.' Similarly, nearly all ethnic minority staff interviewed in the elderly specialty of case study C, reported being regularly racially abused by patients. However, they attempted to make sense of this racial harassment by arguing that it was a product of the patient's confusion, old age and senility. Illness per se was sometimes given as a reason for racism as a nurse working in the general medical specialty in case study F suggested. 'One of the patents said "take your dirty hands off me". You just ignore it. They are ill .... after a while they come round. We never retaliate.' Hence, old age, illness, confusion, mental ill-health, were all given as reasons for the racist behaviour of patients, and nurses often gave the impression that receiving such harassment was simply part of the job, explained by the vulnerable condition of many of the people they were dealing with. Similarly, the racial abuse from patients suffered by minority psychiatric staff was often rationalised by them as part of the patient's psychiatric illness or their old age:

> I know they are not very well so I'm not that sensitive to [all] that. Some [patients] are very abusive and racist [for example] 'go back to where you belong' and 'you're not supposed to be here'.

Or

> There have been several occasions when people have called me names, but I don't take it on board as an insult. I don't get hurt by it. At the end of the day

it is hard to expect people to be nursed by people who are not their own kind, particularly elderly people. I see this as part of the job.

In some workplaces and specialties, such experiences of racial harassment took place on such a regular basis that they had become part of the culture of the workplace.

The study found that a handful of white nurses and midwives also reported being subjected to racial harassment from ethnic minority patients and their families. Within the midwifery specialty of case study D, a white midwife reported having 'difficulties' with some of her black patients. She recounted how 'some of the black patients can be a bit aggressive. They would prefer a West Indian nurse. You have to have a lot of patience to talk to them'. Similarly, in the same employer but a different specialty, another white nurse described how she was racially abused by the friends of a patient she was looking after:

We've had young black patients who have had a crowd of mates come in to visit and when I asked them to leave at eight there has been verbal abuse. I've been called a white ... and if I had taken it down it might have developed into a violent situation. The patient apologised.

In another case study, some white midwifery staff reported that ethnic minority patients occasionally refused to be treated by white staff. However, they recognised that this request was not motivated by racial antagonism against white nurses but rather by cultural difference. As a white midwife recounted, 'if anyone refuses my care they are usually Asian, it's cultural modesty and that's no problem for me'.

Overall, very few white staff reported being racially harassed by black patients. Racial harassment was overwhelmingly a problem faced by ethnic minority staff from white patients.

Racial harassment by colleagues
The preceding section has demonstrated that reports of racial harassment of ethnic minority staff by patients throughout all six case study areas were widespread. In addition, some nurses reported being subjected to racial harassment from colleagues. Although the study found that the extent of racial harassment suffered by ethnic minority nursing staff from colleagues was not as great as that from patients, it remains an issue of concern, particularly in those cases where the perpetrator was identified as being a nurse manager, with control over the allocation of training opportunities and further career development.

In the specialty of community health care in case study A, many of the ethnic minority health visitors and district nurses felt they had been subjected to racial harassment by management and supervisory staff.

Sometimes this took the form of stereotyping ethnic minority groups and being openly disparaging about their ethnicity. An Asian health visitor reported how:

> This made a big impact on me. I was a student health visitor and a manager walked in one morning and forgot that I was there, an Asian girl, and just said 'Oh, those bloody Indians'. Nobody apologised and said look, we didn't mean it ... everyone looked down and carried on working and didn't say anything about it.

Over half of the ethnic minority midwives interviewed in case study D said they had been subjected to incidents of racial harassment by nurse management. Similarly, an ethnic minority auxiliary reported how senior midwifery management interacted in more negative ways with black staff than white staff. Indeed it was not solely the midwifery management but the midwives themselves who often ignored her. She felt this was partly a function of her grade. Unqualified staff were generally not respected or listened to and were often isolated by qualified staff. A white midwife confirmed the existence of racial harassment against ethnic minority staff when she told us how some of her white colleagues made negative comments about ethnic minority midwives.

However, not all white colleagues were supportive of their ethnic minority colleagues and the racial harassment they had to endure. A white midwife explained that any difficulties faced by ethnic minority staff were of their own making:

> Some of the people in our set one in particular thought that they were being 'got at' because they were black. We put it down to her having a chip on her shoulder because she was not treated differently to anyone else [although] she was under the impression that she was treated badly.

In case study E, several ethnic minority nurses said they had been subjected to racial harassment from colleagues and that such racism was a regular feature of their working lives. The racial harassment from colleagues normally took the form of unpleasantness and they felt this was directly related to their 'race' or colour. Similarly, in case study D, some ethnic minority nurses were left with the day-to-day feeling they were not liked, simply because of their colour. Occasionally such situations would lead to confrontations, with one ethnic minority nurse stating how she was 'not being answered when you greet them [white staff], you are ignored'.

The study recorded a small number of incidents where a white nurse felt she had been racially harassed by an ethnic minority colleague. In case study E, a white nurse recounted an incident where:

I was in charge with three black nurses and I had a run in with one of them who wanted to beat me up. I complained to management but because I am white and they were black and I'm not prejudiced at all she was on their side and not mine. She [the manager] said that I must have a problem with colour and it was not that at all ... It's difficult if you complain about someone of a different colour.

In another incident, a white nurse recounted several incidents of 'feeling excluded' by ethnic minority colleagues rather than actually being racially harassed by them. For example, she accused black nurses of being racist because they 'use patois in front of white nurses, excluding them'.

The study also recorded an incident of racial harassment between an Irish nurse and a white English nurse. In the general medical specialty of case study F, an Irish nurse said her working life had been made difficult by white English nurses who 'mocked what I say because of my Irish accent. It's the hardest bit of working here'.

The reporting of incidents of racial harassment and the management response

The study found that most incidents of racial harassment were not reported to senior management. This was because there was a perception amongst ethnic minority victims that their complaints would not be supported by management. Indeed, ethnic minority nursing and midwifery staff felt they were simply expected to ignore such harassment because it was considered unprofessional to be upset or hurt by comments made by patients. Within case study E, ethnic minority nurses who attempted to report such incidents were told 'not to worry' by management. There was little recognition of the nature and effect of such incidents on the working lives of minority nursing staff. Although racial harassment policies existed in every case study area looked at, their coverage was limited to dealing with racist staff and not racist patients. Hence, some ethnic minority staff felt that by failing to address effectively complaints of racial harassment, nurse management were leaving them with the dilemma of having to provide a 'nursing service' to white patients who were openly hostile to them because of their colour.

On those few occasions when senior nurse management sought to tackle the problem, ethnic minority staff thought their response was inadequate. For example, in one community unit studied, senior nursing management, rather than seeking to challenge the racism of patients would seek to 'defuse' the problem by 'warning' potential racist patients that the district nurse that would be visiting them would be from an ethnic minority group,. This had become accepted practice with the district nurse herself having to inform patients over the telephone. Patients who protested at being offered treatment by a nurse from an ethnic minority group or who refused them entry would then be 'warned' by the nurse manager. Some ethnic minority staff saw this as casting an aspersion on their ability to do the job.

Several ethnic minority nurses reported actually being replaced by white nurses in dealing with racist white patients. They felt that this 'pandered to patients' racism'. As stated earlier, most ethnic minority nursing staff interviewed had little confidence in the benefits of reporting such incidents. They were often confused as to whether they could challenge patients who were openly racist or whether they could withdraw their nursing and clinical skills without undermining their professionalism. They did not feel they could be open about their unhappiness at working with racist clients without being seen as 'over-sensitive' or 'unprofessional' by white colleagues and line managers. Nor did they feel that white colleagues and managers would support them in such a decision. Ethnic minority nursing staff had been left to cope with the racial harassment they experienced without support from management. Indeed, managers were not even aware of the scale of the problem in some cases.

Although the study found that ethnic minority nursing staff were far more likely to have been subjected to racial harassment from patients and colleagues than white nursing staff, the level of reporting to management of such incidents was about the same for both groups. In case study C, a white nurse working within the elderly unit spoke of feeling isolated by an ethnic minority ward manager and her minority nursing colleagues. The white nurse had made a formal complaint which was upheld by the employer and the ward manager was 'forced to resign'. This nurse suggested that 'current staff have less obvious chips on their shoulders. The atmosphere is much more amenable, but there is always an undertone. Black nurses are ultra-sensitive'.

Summary and conclusion

The experience of black nurses facing racism is not new. Mary Seacole in 1857 was one of the first black nurses to document it when she said 'they shrink from accepting my help because it flowed from a somewhat duskier skin than theirs' (cited in Alexander and Dewjee 1984). Nearly one hundred and forty years later, racial harassment of ethnic minority nurses continues to be a regular feature of their working lives in the NHS. In every case study area looked at and in nearly every specialty within these areas, ethnic minority nurses reported having been racially harassed by patients. Despite this, they were expected not to 'make a fuss' and to get on with their jobs. They did not have the right to refuse treating the racist patients that were making their working lives so difficult. Many ethnic minority nursing staff had attempted to understand the racial harassment they had experienced from patients as being a function of their illness. On several occasions ethnic minority nurses repeated how they believed that white patients had been racist to them because they suffered from dementia, senility, confusion, old age, mental illness, frustration, anger, or were in extreme pain. As a result, racially abusive behaviour had come to be the 'norm' in the nursing workplace and in some case study areas had become an inextricable aspect of the culture of the workplace.

Racial harassment in the workplace affects the performance of an organisation by creating a climate of isolation and hostility, and this can ultimately detract from the development of an effective and efficient national health service. It will reduce the efficiency and the level of work performance of individual employees and in a wider sense will inhibit the full development of the human resource potential. Externally the corporate image is damaged. This may affect the recruitment and retention of staff, and lessen its ability to provide a service.

Written policies to address the problem of racial harassment and victimisation were not sufficiently comprehensive because they only covered incidents of racial harassment involving fellow colleagues and not patients. As we have already seen, racial harassment from patients was by far the greater problem facing ethnic minority staff. The problem cannot be resolved until management are made aware of the full scale and nature of the problem. A first step would be to encourage victims of racial harassment to report such incidents to nurse managers. This will require a change in workplace culture where ethnic minority nurses feel confident they will be supported by management and that such incidents will be taken seriously, investigated and resolved quickly. Racial harassment policies will be ineffective unless the targets of such mistreatment feel confident enough to complain. Managers need to be aware not only of what constitutes harassment, but that it is a problem within their organisation. Written harassment policies send a clear message from the top of the organisation that racial harassment is unacceptable behaviour. However, within the six case study areas looked at here, the message seemed to have largely stayed at the top, with policies not being translated into effective procedures.

Ellis (1990) in her review of racial equality in the nursing profession outlined a series of action points which could be used to combat racial abuse and harassment at work. In particular, she suggests reinforcing the unacceptability of racist behaviour by patients in general information and publicity materials routinely developed and circulated by health service organisations. This may go some of the way to creating a climate in which racial abuse and harassment becomes unacceptable. Having grievance policies and well-thought out procedures for dealing with both internal and external racial harassment will also help to make the problem unacceptable. Written policies and procedures need to be accompanied by widespread communication, both formally via team briefings and internal memoranda, and informally through more general comments and conversations. It needs to be stressed that 'ignoring it' will not alleviate the problem. Racial harassment will not disappear simply because nursing staff and management refuse to recognise it for fear that it will somehow detract from their 'professionalism'. Instead, it should be made clear that it is precisely because they are professionals that such racist behaviour should not be tolerated from patients or colleagues.

PART III

RESULTS OF THE POSTAL SURVEY

Overview and summary

This national postal survey of nursing and midwifery staff was designed to provide a picture of the progress and experiences of people working as nursing and midwifery staff in the NHS, and, in addition, to support detailed comparisons between members of ethnic minorities and others. The survey collected career history information; details about the current post; information from nursing and midwifery staff about opportunities for training and career development, equal opportunities and experience of racial discrimination and harassment. A total of 14,330 nursing and midwifery staff completed the questionnaire, a response rate of 62 per cent.

The first two chapters in this section concentrate on describing the characteristics of the NHS nursing and midwifery staff, and on building a picture of what is important in career progress for nurses generally. The remaining three chapters in this section look at the ways in which nursing and midwifery staff construe their training opportunities and various aspects of their jobs generally. In summary:

- Chapter 9 begins with a general description of the background characteristics that people bring to nursing jobs, and draws a picture of the nursing and midwifery staff who took part in the study. Approximately eight per cent of the staff were from ethnic minority groups, mainly black and Asian.

- Building on this general picture, Chapter 10 goes on to examine the factors that are associated with progression in the nursing profession, such as levels of nursing qualifications, length of time in the service, and career breaks. Multivariate statistical analyses show that members of certain ethnic groups are more likely to be in lower grades, even after controlling for other factors.

- Chapters 11 and 12 provide more detail on how nursing and midwifery staff perceive opportunities for development in the health service, such as access to training courses. It was found that nurses

139

and midwives experienced difficulties in getting employers to provide paid time-off, and to provide course fee payments. Part-timers and staff on permanent night-duty, felt that they received low priority in the allocation of training. Other aspects of their current job and their working conditions also caused worry and concern for NHS nursing and midwifery staff. In particular, they were not confident that their current grade was correct, and they were dissatisfied with pay, job security and promotion prospects. Despite such concerns, the majority of all nursing and midwifery staff in the study saw their future within the NHS.

• Chapter 13 assesses nursing and midwifery staff relationships with each other and with their patients. Nurses from ethnic minority groups reported extensive experience of racial harassment in their work sometimes from colleagues, often from patients. Well over half of black and Asian nursing and midwifery staff in our survey reported experiencing difficulties with patients for 'racial' reasons. Over a third of all black and Asian nursing staff reported experiencing difficulties with colleagues for 'racial' reasons. Generally, ethnic minority nursing staff felt that they were being discriminated against. Approximately a quarter believed that they had been denied opportunities for training and promotion because of their ethnicity.

The results from the postal questionnaire were weighted to correct for sampling biases, and unless otherwise stated all results are based on the weighted data. Numbers in the body of the tables in this section generally refer to percentages. The total number of nursing and midwifery staff included in each analysis is totalled at the end of each table.

9 A general description of nursing and midwifery staff in the NHS

The NHS nursing and midwifery staff represent a broad section of society and ethnicities. Two questions arise in relation to a general description of the staff members in the PSI survey, based on the results from this cross-sectional snapshot of the nursing professions in the spring of 1994. The first is, what can we find out about nursing staff generally and how do statistics on these 14,000 staff members compare with those presented by other surveys, such as the UKCC reports on NHS nursing staff? Secondly, are ethnic minority staff members any different from their white colleagues in terms of a general description of their backgrounds and characteristics?

Place of birth and ethnic origin
Very little is known about the origin of NHS nursing and midwifery staff in the 1990s, either in terms of their place of birth or their ethnic origin. Place of birth and ethnic origin are, of course, separate concepts. All respondents were asked to say in which country they had been born and, independently, how they would classify their ethnic origin. The questionnaire offered a list of seventeen possible places of birth and offered space to write in additional countries if the list did not provide a suitable option. By far the largest proportion of staff members were born in the United Kingdom (UK) and Northern Ireland. However, altogether nearly two thousand staff (before weighting to adjust for sampling bias) who took part in the survey were born outside the UK and Ireland. The majority of these were born in the Caribbean, Africa or in Asia. Table 9.1 presents the representation of ethnic minority groups in the nursing professions. Like all the tables of results in the report, this is based on the weighted data.

Over 95 per cent of the staff members in the survey were born in five places; the UK, Ireland, the West Indies, Africa and Mauritius. The remaining five per cent were scattered through the world.

In general, this table illustrates the substantial change in hospital staff since earlier studies, in that a far smaller proportion of staff members

141

Table 9.1   Place of birth of NHS nursing staff (based on the 1991 census classification)

Place/area of birth	Per cent
Great Britain & N. Ireland	85.7
Eire/Republic of Ireland	3.5
Rest of Europe	
Germany	0.4
Spain	0.1
Italy	0.1
Poland	<0.1
Caribbean	
West Indies/Guyana	3.0
Indian sub-continent	
India	0.5
Pakistan	0.1
Bangladesh	<0.1
Sri Lanka	0.3
African continent	
Africa	1.4
Mauritius	1.0
Asia	
Malaysia	0.8
Philippines	0.4
Singapore	0.2
Hong Kong	0.2
Vietnam	<0.1
China	<0.1
Australasia	
Australia	0.2
New Zealand	0.1
North America	
Canada	0.1
USA	0.1
Other	
Cyprus	0.1
Malta	0.1
Other	0.9
Not stated	0.6
Total nursing staff	14,330

were born abroad. The figures suggested that nearly 90 per cent of members of the NHS nursing and midwifery staff in the study in the spring of 1994 were born in the UK or Eire. There were few staff members from the rest of Europe, the United States, or from Australia and New Zealand. The large proportion who were born in the UK will partly be a reflection of the fact that these were permanent staff, and there is likely to be a slightly higher proportion of foreign nursing staff (for example, Australians) working temporarily in the NHS as part of a break from their home country. A relatively small group of respondents (one per cent) chose not to answer the question.

The next question asked about ethnic origin. Altogether, 1,630 people from ethnic minority groups completed the questionnaire, representing the largest group of ethnic minority nursing and midwifery staff ever surveyed. The initial hope had been to include at least 1,000 nursing and midwifery staff belonging to ethnic minority groups, to support detailed

Table 9.2 Ethnic origin of NHS nursing staff

Ethnic origin	Per cent
White	84
Black Caribbean	3
Indian	1
Black African	1
Chinese	1
Indian Caribbean	<1
Mauritian	<1
Filipino	<1
White other	<1
Pakistani	<1
Sri Lankan	<1
Bangladeshi	<1
Black other	1
Not stated	7
Total nursing staff	14,440

The total of nurses is 14,330, so some have answered two categories.

career progress analyses, so the postal survey was very successful in this respect. After the weighting adjustments, the overwhelming majority of respondents (82 per cent) categorised themselves as white. The next most frequent response was Black Caribbean (four per cent), followed by Indian and Black Africans who both represented two per cent of the responses, and the Chinese with one per cent.

The weighted ethnic minority grouping figures are presented in Table 9.2. This suggests that, on a national level (counting the non-respondents as a separate group), approximately eight per cent of nursing and midwifery staff belong to ethnic minority groups. In addition, it is important that we assume that a proportion of those who chose not to answer the question will also be from ethnic minority groups, and the figure of eight per cent thus probably represents an underestimate.

Table 9.3   Area of birth of those who did not answer ethnic origin questions

Percentages

Area of birth	Nursing staff not answering ethnic origin question born in each area
United Kingdom & N. Ireland	92
Eire/Irish Republic	2
West Indies/Guyana	1
Mauritius	<1
Africa	<1
Germany	<1
Philippines	<1
India	<1
Sri Lanka	<1
Other	<1
Not stated	3
Total nursing staff	1,076

The question concerning how staff members would describe their ethnic origin produced rather more non-respondents than the question on place of origin, with seven per cent of nursing staff choosing not to answer. Table 9.3 shows where those not answering the ethnicity question were born. The vast majority of those not answering the ethnic origin question were born in the UK. As this does not clarify their ethnic origin, it was not possible to make any guess as to their potential ethnic grouping. However, given the size of the group, they are kept in most subsequent analyses presented in this part as a separate group, distinct from the other white, black and Asian groups. As later tables will demonstrate, the manner in which they respond to various questions is nearly always sufficiently different from any of the main ethnic groupings to suggest that they are a heterogeneous group, probably containing some white nursing staff and some ethnic minority group members as well. The question remains concerning why these staff members chose not to answer the ethnicity question, and this requires further research.

Given the wide range of responses, and in order to create groups large enough to base analyses on, it was necessary to simplify the ethnic groupings. Table 9.4 shows the simplification used in most of the subsequent analyses. Grouping ethnicities is very difficult, as there are no hard and fast rules about which groups should go together and there are, of course, always other alternative groupings that could have been used. However, grouping of ethnic minority groups is essential to provide groups of meaningful size for comparison with the white staff members. For the purposes of these analyses, the various ethnic groups were grouped into four main categories reflecting original geographic and ethnic affiliation. The first group is 'white', including Eire and the United States, and Australia as well as white British.

Black groups from both Africa and the Caribbean were classified together, along with the 'Black other' group, into the Black group. This was the second largest group after the 'White' group.

The third main ethnic group was classified as 'Asian', and included people from the Indian subcontinent and those who may have migrated from other areas such as the Caribbean, but who called themselves 'Indian'.

The fourth group contained those nursing and midwifery staff who specified a clear ethnic group which could not be sensibly classified into either of the first three groups, but were not of a sufficient size to stand alone as a separate classification. Examples include 'Chinese', 'Malaysian', 'South American Indian', and 'Arab'. In addition, any who named mixed ethnicity combinations without specifying any weight to one or the other part were included in this third category. These included answers such as 'Creole Mauritian' and 'Indian-Chinese'.

Table 9.4   Shortened ethnic origin of NHS nursing staff

Ethnic code	Includes	Number of nursing staff	Per cent
White	White Irish European	12,056	84
Black	Black Caribbean Black African Black other	624	4
Asian	Indian Pakistani Bangladeshi Indian Caribbean Sri Lankan Mauritian	348	2
Other	Chinese Filipino Malaysian Mixed ethnicity (if no main ethnic group stated)	225	2
Not stated		1,076	8
Total nursing staff		14,440	

Those who answered two categories of ethnic origin were assigned to one only, so the figures vary slightly from Table 9.2 above.

There were too many of those omitting to answer the ethnicity question altogether either to place them in one of the first four categories, or to justify excluding them, and so the final group of 'Not stated' was created to contain them. They are generally included in analyses and treated as a separate, miscellaneous group.

Demographic details
All nursing and midwifery staff were asked basic background questions concerning sex, age, marital status and housing tenure. These questions provide important descriptive information on the sample, and allow for comparison with other information on staff members such as that provided routinely by the UKCC on qualified nurses and midwives. The

UKCC data are UK wide, whereas the PSI survey was of staff based in England only. However, there is no reason to believe that the patterns in the two data sets should be different and the UKCC data provide a useful comparison.

Overall, only seven per cent of the nursing and midwifery staff in the survey were male. The Department of Health figures for the NHS workforce (Department of Health 1991) suggest that on the 30 September 1989, of all nursing and midwifery staff, 11 per cent of the total were male. When these figures were adjusted to 'whole-time equivalents' (counting two half-time workers as one whole-time worker, for example), the figure dropped slightly to 10 per cent. The Department of Health do not present these figures by ethnicity, so direct comparisons are not possible. They do suggest, however, that at seven per cent overall, the numbers of male nursing staff are a little lower than expected amongst these respondents. This could be due to a number of reasons. It may be that the figures have changed since 1989, because the structure of the nursing staff will have changed over the past six years. It was also possible that we had a slightly lower than expected rate of response from male nursing staff compared with female nursing staff, or that the sampling procedure missed areas where male nursing staff were most concentrated.

Table 9.5   Sex of NHS nursing staff by ethnic origin

Percentages

Ethnic origin	Women	Men
White	93	7
Black	90	10
Asian	73	27
Other	83	17
Not stated	95	5
Total nursing staff	13,243	1,035

Some nurses did not state their sex, thus the total is slightly less than 14,330.

Table 9.5 shows the relative sex ratios of the staff members from the different ethnic groups. Within the overall rate of seven per cent male, there were variations in the proportion of men among the different groups, most noticeably in the Asian group, where just over one quarter of the nursing staff were male. As there are no comparable statistics, this is a new and surprising finding and one that requires further investigation. If the different ethnic groups are found to be concentrated in different grades and specialties, it will be important to return to this uneven sex distribution.

The nursing and midwifery staff in the PSI study were, on average, forty years old (in this report, 'average' always refers to the statistical mean). Their ages varied from 16 years old to 69 years old. From this first glance, the staff members seem to be a little older than might be expected. This is likely to be due in part to the fact that the sample includes only permanent staff (and excludes students and bank staff) and perhaps temporary staff are slightly younger. In order to check the age of this sample of permanent staff members against a national statistic for nurses, all qualified nurses were separated from the unqualified and auxiliary staff and their ages were grouped into five categories for comparison with statistics from the UKCC on nurses on the Council's Professional Register (UKCC 1991). This comparison is presented in Figure 9.1.

Figure 9.1   Comparison of PSI and UKCC age distributions for qualified nursing staff

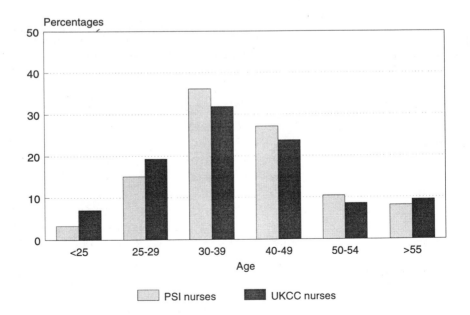

From UKCC stats, 1990-1991

Approximately similar numbers of PSI nursing and midwifery staff and UKCC nurses fall into the different age categories, although slightly more PSI nursing staff than UKCC nurses fall into the middle 30-39 and 40-49 groups, and slightly fewer into the outlying groups of those under 29 or over 55 years. The UKCC do not break these figures down so it is not possible to compare the average ages of both groups. However, the figure suggests that, despite the fact that the distribution of age for the PSI sample is more clustered in the middle, the average ages for the PSI and UKCC groups would be approximately similar at around 40 years.

In addition to the UKCC figures, the Department of Health also present figures on characteristics of the workforce, and the 1991 edition (DoH 1991) again suggests that the largest proportion of nursing and midwifery staff fell in the 30-39 age group, with 18 per cent of the nursing and midwifery staff between 25 and 29, 23 per cent between 30 and 39, and 22 per cent between 40 and 49 (DoH 1991: pB14 Table B1.9). The spread of nursing and midwifery staff across the age range was broader again in the DOH figures than the UKCC figures, with fairly large proportions falling under age 25 (21 per cent) or over 50 (14 per cent). However, comparisons are difficult as these figures refer to all nursing and midwifery staff, except they exclude agency and locum nurses. Overall, with reference to age, it would seem that the PSI sample is not dissimilar from other samples of nursing and midwifery staff.

Moving on to a comparison of the ages of the different ethnic groups represented in the nursing and midwifery staff, Figure 9.2 shows the average age of permanent staff members by ethnic origin. As the figure shows, the white nursing and midwifery staff were younger than their comparisons in the ethnic minorities by approximately four years. The differences between the different minority groups were slight, although the black group were the oldest at 45 years old on average. The white group were statistically significantly younger than the ethnic minority groups, with an average of 40 years old. It will be important to bear this in mind when comparing the relative positions reached within the profession by members of the different ethnic groups.

Three-quarters of the staff members who took part in the survey were married or living with someone at the time they responded. This might be partly a reflection of the age of the group, as by the time the general population reaches their late 30s and early 40s, rates of cohabitation will be at their highest. It may also reflect the permanent nature of their jobs, as on the whole this will be a relatively stable population. There were minor variations between the ethnic minority groups, this time most noticeably for the black group where more nursing and midwifery staff

Figure 9.2   Average age of nursing staff by ethnic origin

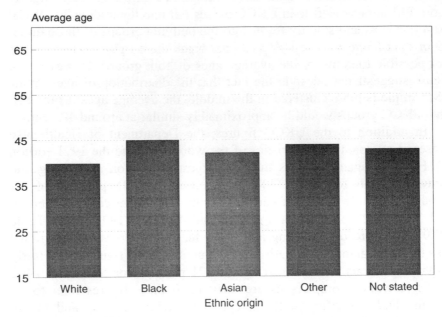

Average age

F=64.5, df 14143 p<.0001

were single, widowed or divorced (37 per cent). These figures are similar to other national estimates which suggest that black people have a slightly higher chance of being single or separated than other groups (see, for example, Jones 1993).

Table 9.6   Marital status of nursing staff by ethnic origin

Percentages

Ethnic origin	Married or cohabiting	Single, widowed or divorced
White	77	23
Black	63	37
Asian	78	22
Other	79	21
Not stated	80	20
Total nursing staff	10,821	3,346

167 nursing staff did not answer the question.

Table 9.7 reflects the large numbers who were living with others by showing that the majority of those taking part were in privately owned or privately rented accommodation. Only a very small group were in NHS accommodation. Housing tenure might reflect a number of different factors including personal (such as age), cultural and financial. The large numbers in privately owned accommodation again suggests that this was a relatively stable group. There were few differences between the groups, with slightly fewer blacks living in their own accommodation, and slightly more of the 'other' group doing so. More blacks were living in council accommodation (10 per cent, compared to rates of approximately 4 per cent for other groups). Other surveys of ethnic minority populations have also suggested this to be the case in the general population as a whole (Jones 1993, Brown 1984).

Table 9.7   Current housing situation by ethnic origin

Percentages

Accommodation type	White	Black	Asian	Other	Not stated
Privately owned	86	76	84	91	86
Privately rented	6	5	5	3	4
NHS accommodation	2	3	3	1	1
Council	4	10	3	2	4
Housing association	1	3	3	1	1
Other	1	3	2	2	4
Total nursing staff	12,056	624	348	225	1,076

103 nursing staff members did not answer the question.

Many of the nursing and midwifery staff had children under the age of 16 at the time they completed the questionnaires. Figure 9.3 shows the percentage of men and women in each of the ethnic groups with children under 16. In both the white and black groups, approximately 40 per cent of the nursing and midwifery staff had children of this age. Rather more of the Asians and the 'other' group did so: 56 per cent of the former and 50 per cent of the latter. Once again, the group of staff members who did not answer the question did not particularly resemble any of the other groups. In this case, fewer of them had young children than the rest of the sample.

Figure 9.3 Men and women nursing staff with children under 16 by ethnic group

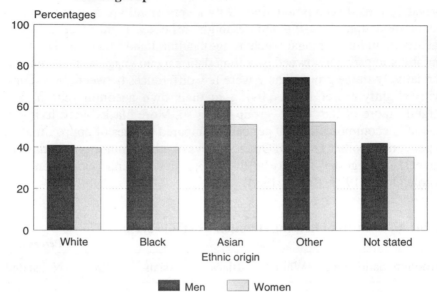

In all groups, men were more likely to have children under 16, this being particularly the case for the mixed ethnicity ('other') group.

In summary, the nursing and midwifery staff in the PSI survey were, on average, 40 years old, although age varied by ethnic group with the white group being several years younger than the ethnic minority groups. In all the ethnic groups, women outnumbered men, and overall over 90 per cent of the staff members were female. However, a higher proportion of the Asian group were male than any of the other groups. Approximately half of the nursing and midwifery staff had children under 16, three-quarters were living with spouses or cohabitees, and most were in accommodation that they either owned or rented privately.

Qualifications

A variety of different measures of qualifications were used in the survey. In this section the general qualifications that nursing and midwifery staff bring to nursing are examined.

A scale comprising the highest level of educational qualification reached was devised. The levels were GCSE passes at Grade C or above, or their equivalent, A levels or equivalent, ONCs or equivalent, HNCs or equivalent, and university degree or PhD.

Table 9.8 shows how general educational qualifications were related to three main types of staff members in the project; auxiliary, enrolled

Table 9.8   Levels of general education by type of nursing staff

Percentages

Highest level of general education reached	Nurse type		
	Auxiliary	Enrolled	Registered
No general qualifications	66	38	11
O levels or equivalent	25	51	45
A levels or equivalent	2	4	20
ONCs or equivalent	5	4	5
HNCs or equivalent	1	3	14
Degree or above	1	1	5

Total nursing staff   14,242

The level of education could not be calculated for 88 nursing staff.

and registered. Unqualified nursing staff had the lowest level of general education, and registered nurses had the highest level, reflecting the fact that there are minimum entry requirements to the different grades.

Figure 9.4 compares the average level of education reached for each of the ethnic groupings. From this it is possible to see that the Asian, 'other' and white nursing and midwifery staff had the most qualifications, while the black group had the lowest scores.

Figure 9.4   Average general education score by ethnic origin

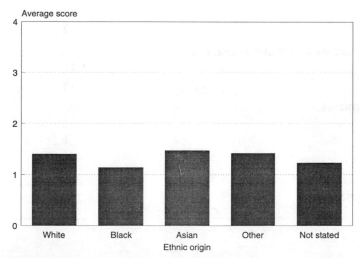

F=40.9, df 10161,4 p<.0001

Grading

As described in Part 1, nursing and midwifery staff are graded on a scale from A (unqualified) to I (most senior). In general (although there is some variation), Grades A and B are unqualified nursing and midwifery staff, grades C, D, E and F represent the enrolled nurses, registered nurses and core professional grades, and the highest grades, G, H and I, represent managers, senior nurses and team leaders. Qualified staff working in the community also tend to be graded G or above, such as health visitors, district nurses and community midwives. Respondents indicated that they were distributed across the grading structure in the manner expected, with the majority of staff members to be found in the middle grades of D and E. Table 9.9 shows that approximately 22 per cent of the nursing staff in this national survey were in the unqualified A and B grades, approximately 43 per cent fell into the middle grades of C, D and E, and the remaining third were graded F or above.

Table 9.9   Grading structure of nursing staff

Percentages

Grade	Nursing staff in each grade
Unqualified	
A	18
B	4
Staff nurses (core professional grades)	
C	3
D	18
E	22
Charge nurses and ward managers	
F	11
G	18
Senior nurses	
H	3
I	1
Not stated	1
Total nursing staff	14,330

Table 9.10   Grade of NHS nursing staff by ethnic origin

Percentages

Grade	White	Black	Asian	Other	Not stated
Unqualified					
A	17	21	11	10	22
B	4	6	3	2	4
Staff nurses (core professional grades)					
C	3	3	5	4	3
D	19	21	17	13	13
E	22	21	29	28	20
Charge nurses and ward managers					
F	11	9	9	11	11
G	18	16	19	28	19
Senior nurses					
H	3	3	5	2	4
I	1	1	2	2	1
Not stated	1	2	1	1	4
Total	12,056	624	348	225	1,076

Did the distribution of ethnic groups across the grading structure show any differences to this pattern? Table 9.10 shows the grading pattern for the distribution of the main ethnic minority groups.

Despite the differences in general qualifications shown in the previous section, Table 9.10 suggests that the ethnic minority groups are relatively well represented in the higher grades. In fact, the two groups best represented in the higher grades of F and above are the 'other' group and the Asian group, with 44 per cent of the first and 36 per cent of the second with grades of F or higher. Representation for white and black nurses in these higher grades is similar to each other, at 34 and 31 per cent respectively.

Other figures to note in the table include the relative under-representation of Asian staff members in the unqualified grades, with their corresponding over-representation in the middle staff nurse grades.

Black nurses were nearly twice as likely as the Asians to be unqualified nursing staff (27 per cent compared to 14 per cent).

From what we already know about these staff members, those from ethnic minority groups tended to be older, and it is possible that they might be under-represented in the higher grades if age were taken into account. The next chapter will look at the more complex interactions between the various factors that might contribute to grading, such as qualifications, age, sex and length in the profession, in order to untangle patterns that might underlie the distribution of the various ethnic groups across the various grades. However, the grading patterns presented in Table 9.10 suggest that, at this initial stage, certain ethnic minority groups were doing as well as their white peers in the general NHS nursing hierarchy.

Specialties

Nursing specialties vary considerably in terms of the nature of the work, the range of grades they usually represent, the qualifications needed, and how they are perceived by the nursing and medical community. Specialties based in the community, for example, tend to be associated with higher grades as an additional, post-basic qualification, is often needed

Figure 9.5 Distribution of all nursing and midwifery staff across the different specialties

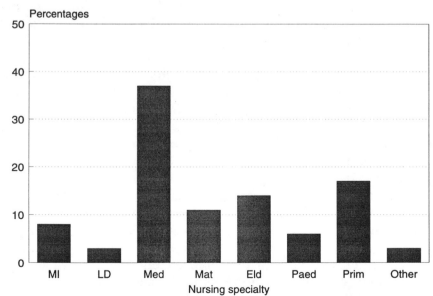

Table 9.11 Nursing specialty by ethnic group

Percentages

Nursing specialty	White	Black	Asian	Other	Not stated
Mental illness	7	13	21	21	6
Learning disability	3	6	10	8	2
Medical/Surgical	38	26	28	25	36
Maternity	12	12	9	16	10
Elderly	14	22	14	12	15
Paediatric	6	5	3	4	5
Community	17	14	12	14	22
Other	2	2	3	1	3
Total nursing staff	11,919	601	344	222	1,039

181 nursing staff members did not answer the question.

for them. Certain specialties are considered to carry more status than others. The next section makes another preliminary step in the analyses by looking at the distribution of nursing and midwifery staff across the specialties, including ethnic minority nurses and midwifery staff.

The nursing specialties were grouped broadly according to the Department of Health classifications used in their report on the NHS workforce (Department of Health 1991). General medical included the various medical specialties mentioned such as working in a burns unit, in opthalmics or in plastic surgery. Midwives, and those in gynaecological specialties were classified as 'Maternity'. The 'Community' group included all those working away from the hospital (apart from community midwives), including health visitors, those working in schools and in General Practice (GP) surgeries. Approximately one per cent of the staff members did not answer the question about specialty. Nursing staff were only given one option.

Figure 9.5 shows the distribution of all nursing and midwifery staff across the different specialties.

The two most common specialties for staff members to be working in were medical and primary (community) health care. These were followed by working with the elderly, and working in maternity.

When comparisons are made between the distributions of the ethnic origin groups across the specialties (Table 9.11), patterns emerge which confirm previous anecdotal information concerning the over-representation of ethnic minority nursing staff in some areas, particularly those considered under-resourced and 'low-tech'. There were, for example, proportionally more black nursing staff than any other group in care of the elderly (nearly a quarter), and more Asians working with mental illness and learning disability (nearly a third altogether). In the specialties that are traditionally regarded as of higher status, such as medical and primary (community) health care, the white staff members retain the highest proportions, with over a third of white nurses in medical specialties, for example.

The differences were most striking for mental illness and learning disability. In both cases, approximately twice as many black nursing staff and three times as many Asian and 'other' nursing staff were working, compared with white nursing staff.

In general, these patterns support much of the existing commentary on ethnicity and nursing, most of which has suggested that this type of concentration in the 'lower status' specialties as they are sometimes known is common.

These differences in the specialties in which ethnic minority staff members tend to be concentrated may be important in considering their progress within the nursing profession. It may be easier, for example, to reach the higher grades in which we saw that they were well represented overall in the more unpopular specialties.

Working arrangements
In addition to being concentrated in various areas of work, nursing and midwifery staff will also vary in the types of working patterns they adopt. The majority of the staff members in the study (54 per cent) had full-time jobs, although large numbers were working part-time (45 per cent). Job sharing arrangements were very rare, with only one per cent of nursing and midwifery staff having a job share.

Table 9.12 shows the differences between the ethnic minority groups in terms of the proportions working part-time versus full-time. Generally, part-time work was taken to be work of less than 35 hours a week. Given the interest in flexible working hours within the profession, staff members were given the opportunity to say that they were in a job share arrangement. Very few were. These figures show that a significantly larger proportion of white staff members were working part-time, when compared with the ethnic minority groups. Nearly half the former and one third of the latter had part-time jobs. Here the similarities between the ethnic minority groups, when compared to the white group, stand out.

Table 9.12 Working pattern by ethnic group

Ethnic origin	Full-time	Part-time	Job share
White	53	46	1
Black	70	30	–
Asian	66	34	–
Other	66	34	–
Not stated	50	49	1
Overall	7,039	5,944	153

Working full-time might also raise the chances of progressing faster in the nursing profession, and given these differences between the groups, it will be important to consider the contribution of type of employment to career progress in the next chapter.

The variety of different shifts represented within the nursing workplace is very large. As Table 9.13 shows, the majority of all nursing and midwifery staff were working one of four shifts; a mix of earlies, lates and nights; days only; nights only; or a mix of earlies and lates. They are usually referred to as earlies, lates and nights or days only. Early shifts are those which start after the night shift has finished, typically between 7 and 8am. Late shifts are those that begin after the early shift has finished. Late shifts typically start between 2 and 3pm and last until the night shift begins, typically between 9 and 10pm. Day shifts only reflect working hours usually between 8am and 6pm.

To make comparisons simpler between the ethnic groups, the shifts were classified into four main patterns as shown on the table. Overall at the time of the survey, over half the nursing and midwifery staff were working rotations (53 per cent), a quarter were working days (25 per cent), 17 per cent were working some variation on lates and nights, and the remaining 5 per cent were working to some other arrangement. It has been suggested that night staff are disadvantaged in terms of clinical grading, as they might be less likely to receive classification as management. Figure 9.6 shows the differences between the ethnic groups in terms of these four main types of shift-work.

Finally, it is not unusual for nursing and midwifery staff to supplement their NHS work with other jobs, and in this study, just over a

Table 9.13 Nursing staff shift patterns

Shift	Per cent of nursing staff
Rotating	
Mix E, L & N	27
Mix E & L	25
Days only	
Days 9-5	23
Days 9-3	2
Mornings only	1
Earlies only	2
Lates and evenings only	
Nights	16
Lates only	<1
Evenings	1
Other	
Split shifts	1
Flexi	2
As required	<1
On call	<1
Other	1
Not stated	1
Total answers	14,621
Total nursing staff	14,330

fifth of nursing and midwifery staff had another source of paid work. Despite the fact that the ethnic minority groups were more likely already to be working full-time than the white nursing and midwifery staff, Table 9.14 shows that they were also more likely to be doing extra paid work on top of their NHS jobs. This is perhaps more likely for employees in certain specialties such as mental illness, learning disability and care of the elderly, where twelve hour shifts for three-day weeks are not uncommon. Again, the similarities between the ethnic minority groups are striking, with a quarter or more of black, Asian and mixed ethnicity staff members doing other paid work.

Figure 9.6 Shift work patterns by ethnic group

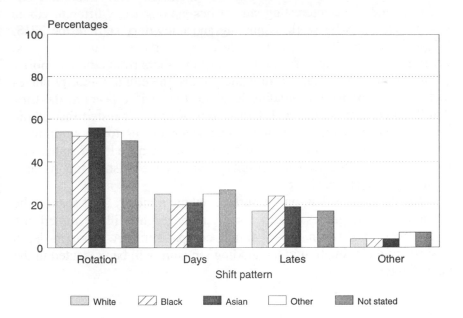

In this respect, the lives of ethnic minority nursing and midwifery staff in the NHS seem to involve more hours of work than their colleagues, and thus, potentially, more stress.

Table 9.14 Other paid work by ethnic group

Ethnic origin	Per cent doing other paid work
White	19
Black	28
Asian	26
Other	25
Not stated	15
Total nursing staff	14,194

136 of nursing staff members did not answer the question

Conclusion

These cross-sectional analyses begin to highlight some important differences, and some interesting similarities, amongst the different ethnic group members who work as nursing and midwifery staff in the NHS. Primarily, although there were differences in the sex ratios, age and general educational qualifications of staff members from ethnic minority groups compared to those from white groups, the ethnic minority nurses had attained comparable grading levels to their white peers at the time that the study was conducted. Other comparisons suggested that ethnic minority nurses were more likely than white nurses to be working in certain specialties, particularly those considered to have lower status, and to be working full-time. These results confirm some existing reports such as that by Akinsanya (1988).

Despite the fact that, on the surface, ethnic minority staff seem to be reaching similar grades to other staff, there might still be underlying differences masked in these simple comparisons. A more in-depth analysis of their situation in the grading structure will be presented in the next chapter.

10 Career history and progress

In addition to their personal characteristics, such as sex and age, and the general educational qualifications that they bring to nursing, staff members will vary greatly in terms of different aspects of their nursing careers. These variations include the different nursing qualifications that they have accrued, the length of time they have been in the nursing profession, the number of career breaks that they have taken, and the time they have spent in their current post. These variables are also likely to be related to their position in the grading hierarchy and it will be important to take them into account when building up a model to predict nursing grade, and in assessing the independent, additional role played by ethnicity in predicting their current position.

Nursing qualifications

Nursing qualifications are varied and complicated, and difficult to compare. As outlined in Chapter 1, until relatively recently nurses qualified initially as either enrolled or registered nurses. Enrolled nurses may convert to become registered by doing a conversion course. In addition to their basic qualification, nurses may specialise in certain areas and go on to take post-basic courses.

Table 10.1 lists the main, basic, qualifications acquired by the staff members in the survey. Many nurses will also have certificates and diplomas in various specialties, but these are not listed here.

For simplicity, on the basis of the long list of qualifications acquired by the nursing staff, which included those listed above *and* their post-basic qualifications, the whole sample was split into five; those who were unqualified nursing staff; those who had qualifications indicating that they were enrolled nurses; those who were enrolled nurses and also had extra post-basic qualifications; those who had qualifications indicating they were registered nurses, including those with degrees in nursing; and a final group of those who had post-registration qualifications on top of their registration. Midwives were classified as nurses with post-registration qualifications although there will be some

Table 10.1 **Nursing qualifications (excluding post-basic courses)**

Qualification	Abbreviation	Per cent of nursing staff
Unqualified		22
Enrolled nurse	EN	19
Enrolled nurse (mental handicap)	EN (MH)	2
Registered general nurse/ State registered nurse	RGN/SRN	58
Registered mental nurse	RMN	7
Registered mental handicap nurse	RNMH	2
Registered sick children's nurse	RSCN	3
Registered midwife/ State certified midwife	RM, SCM	14
Registered health visitor	RHV, HV	4
Registered nurse tutor	RNT	
Registered clinical nurse tutor	RCNT	
National district nurse	NDN	4
BA/BSC Nursing	BA/BSc	1
Total nursing staff	14,330	

pre-registration midwives in this group. Nurses whose initial qualification was a degree in nursing were classified with the registered nurses without post-registration qualifications. The post-registration category reflects nurses who have gone on, beyond their initial qualification, to study for something further, and was intended to reflect some further investment in career qualifications. Nurses with degrees *and* some further specialisation were thus included in the top group. The classification reflects a hierarchy from least qualifications to most qualifications, and each nurse received a score based on his or her highest level of qualification reached. This score ranged from 0 to 4. In addition, there was a small group of staff members who failed to supply information about their qualifications but who were of grade C and above (and thus cannot be assumed to be unqualified), and these did not receive a nursing qualification score.

Figure 10.1 Average nursing qualification score for nursing staff in each grade (A-I)

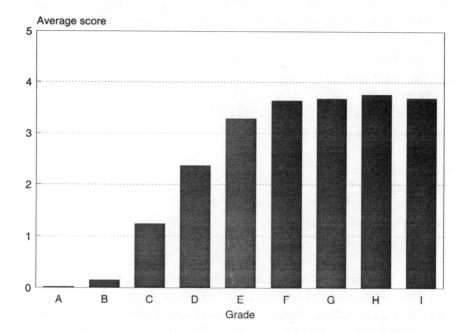

Figure 10.1 plots the average score of staff members in each of the nursing grades, from A (unqualified) to I (highest grade). This demonstrates a clear and positive relationship between nursing qualifications and nursing grade, with nursing staff in every subsequent grade above A up to H having proportionally more nursing qualifications. The relationship is strongest at the bottom of the nursing hierarchy where the jumps in average nursing qualifications are relatively large from grade to grade, and reaches a plateau at the top of the nursing hierarchy, where there is little difference in nursing qualifications between those who are grades G, H and I.

Table 10.2 shows how ethnic minority staff members compared with white nursing staff on this five-way classification.

The pattern was not entirely straightforward. On the one hand, there were many similarities between the groups. The majority of all the nurse groups were registered nurses (with or without post-registration qualifications), and this is so for all the groups. Similar proportions were enrolled nurses with extra qualifications.

On the other hand, there were some differences. The most noticeable of these were not between the ethnic minority groups and the white staff

Table 10.2 Highest nursing qualification by ethnic origin

Grade	White	Black	Asian	Other	NS
Unqualified/auxiliary	21	26	13	12	26
Enrolled nurses	10	15	15	13	9
Enrolled nurse plus extra quals	4	6	5	5	3
Registered nurses	28	21	33	27	25
Registered nurses plus extra quals	36	31	33	43	37
Missing, but probably qualified	1	1	1	1	1
Total nursing staff	12,056	624	348	225	1,076

members, but between the various ethnic minority groups themselves. The black staff and those from unstated ethnic origins had the highest rates of unqualified members. One of the most striking comparisons was the difference between them and the Asians, who had the lowest rate of unqualified staff members, half that of the black staff, and just over half that of the white staff.

Slightly smaller proportions of black staff members were registered nurses compared with the other groups. The mixed ethnicity group had the highest rate, followed by the Asians. In most of these comparisons, the qualifications of the white group fell somewhere in between those of the other various ethnic groups.

Length of time in the profession

The nursing and midwifery staff in the study had generally been in the nursing professions for many years by the time they took part in the survey. This will again be a function partly of the permanent nature of their jobs, and of their age. Respondents estimated how long they had been nursing and midwifery staff, after subtracting any time out of the profession taking a career break or doing something else. On average, they had worked as NHS staff members for 171 months (just over 14 years), excluding breaks.

The length of time that nursing and midwifery staff had spent in the nursing professions was also positively related to the level that they had

Figure 10.2 Length of time in the profession by grade

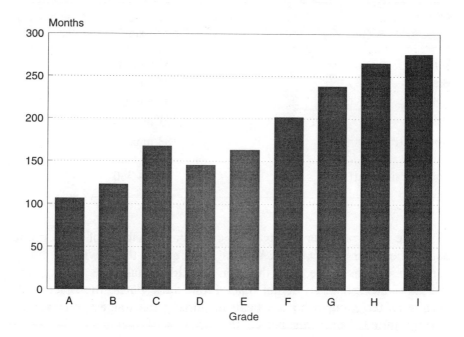

reached on the nursing hierarchy. Figure 10.2 plots the average length of time that staff members in each of the grades had been in the nursing profession, as measured from the date of their first job as a staff member. Although it was generally true that the longer nursing and midwifery staff had been in the profession the higher their grade, the relationship was not as clear cut as that between nursing qualifications and grade. Thus, for example, Grade D nurses had been in nursing, on average, for approximately two years less than either Grade C or Grade E. This may be due to the fact that many registered nurses enter the grading hierarchy at Grade D, bringing the average down for that grade. The relationship at the top end of the grading hierarchy is clear, and Grade I nurses were those who had been NHS nursing and midwifery staff for the longest period.

The previous chapter showed that the different ethnic groups were mainly equally distributed across the grading hierarchy, but the chapter also showed that ethnic minority staff members were older than the white staff. Have they also been nursing and midwifery staff for longer than white staff on average? Table 10.3 shows that indeed they have, and all three main ethnic minority groups had been nursing and midwifery staff for approximately two years more than the white staff.

Table 10.3 Length of time in the nursing profession by ethnic group

Ethnic origin	Average length of time in the nursing profession, in months
White	168 months
Black	191 months
Asian	192 months
Other	191 months
Not stated	183 months
Total nursing staff	14,330

F=15.3, p<.001

Table 10.4 presents the average year that members of each group began their nursing careers. Within each group there will be much variation on this score, and the year should be taken as a summary indicator rather than an actual date. From these dates, the black staff emerge as the group who has been in nursing the longest, on average having started four years before the white staff members. The other ethnic groups fall between these two extremes.

One final comparison confirms this conclusion: nursing and midwifery staff were asked what year they got their first job as a nurse or nursing auxiliary. This measure does not exclude breaks of any kind but again the same pattern is seen, with ethnic minority nursing and midwifery staff having begun their nursing jobs or careers at an earlier point than their white peers.

Table 10.4 Average year first started nursing by ethnic origin

Ethnic origin	Average year started
White	1979
Black	1975
Asian	1977
Other	1976
Not stated	1977
Overall	1978

Time in current post

On average, nursing and midwifery staff had been in their current post for a substantial amount of time, 88 months (seven years), at the time that they filled in the questionnaire. Given that, on average, they had been in the profession for fourteen years, this represented about half of their nursing career.

There were strong differences between the average lengths of time that the ethnic groups had been in their posts. These are shown in Table 10.5. The white group had been in their posts for the shortest time, 84 months on average. The black staff members had been in theirs for the longest time, 125 months. The remainder of the groups fell somewhere in between.

This result might be an indicator that the white nursing and midwifery staff were moving up the grades faster than their ethnic minority peers. Alternatively, it could reflect more movement across posts within the same level, rather than a move upwards. The most likely explanation, however, is that it was a reflection of the fact that they had been in the profession as a whole for a shorter time than the ethnic minority staff (as Table 10.3 showed).

Table 10.5 Length of time in current post by ethnic group

Ethnic origin	Average length of time in current post in months
White	84 months
Black	125 months
Asian	111 months
Other	120 months
Not stated	95 months
Total nursing staff	14,330

$F=58.83$, df 4,14325, $p<.001$

Career breaks

Nursing and midwifery staff were asked to total the number of breaks, if any, that they had taken from their nursing service, and to give the main reason for these breaks. Most frequently, career breaks in nursing are given for up to five years to deal with child-care responsibilities. Occasionally they can be for periods of study. Staff returning from breaks for family reasons have to compete for vacant posts. Promoted posts are few and far between. The NHS has agreed that staff should be able to return at the same grade as they left, but there is no central monitoring of this yet.

Over half of the staff members (56 per cent) had taken at least one career break, which was not surprising given the average length of their service and the fact that most of them were women. Most of those taking breaks had only taken one – 29 per cent of all nursing and midwifery staff had taken one break. A fifth had taken two breaks, and three per cent had taken nine or more breaks.

Table 10.6 lists the main reasons for career breaks, demonstrating as expected that the majority of breaks were taken to cover child-care responsibilities. However, the second most common reason for taking a break was to do another job, so although the total length of service in the NHS was long on average, quite a few members of the nursing and midwifery staff were moving in and out of employment with the NHS over the years, either to do another job entirely or to work as private nurses.

Table 10.6 Reasons for career breaks, ranked in order of frequency mentioned

Percentages

Reason for break	Nurses having taken a break due to each reason
Children	45
Other job	12
Private nursing	10
Nursing abroad	5
Unemployment	3
Education	2
Time out (holidays & travel)	2
Bank nursing	<1
Ill health	<1
GP surgery	<1
Family planning	<1
Total nursing staff	14,330

It is commonly thought that career breaks are detrimental to career development, and it might be assumed that nursing and midwifery staff who have taken career breaks, or several career breaks, will be concentrated in the lower or middle grades of the nursing hierarchy. To simplify the comparison between the different grades, the grading hierarchy was blocked into three: unqualified (A & B); core professional grades (C, D & E); and senior grades (F and above. The number of staff who had taken career breaks in each of the three grade blocks was compared (see Table 10.7).

Table 10.7 Career breaks and grading structure: Are nursing staff in the higher grades less likely to have taken career breaks?

Percentages

Number of career breaks	Grade level		
	A & B	C, D & E	F +
0	75	41	29
1	17	30	34
2	6	20	25
3-9	2	10	12
10+	<1	<1	<1
Total nursing staff	3,034	6,230	4,772

Taking career breaks, even multiple career breaks, does not seem to have been negatively related to progress within the profession in that the nurses in the higher grades were actually more likely to have taken career breaks than those who were in the lower grades or who were unqualified. This simply suggests that, rather than holding staff members back, the longer they have been in the profession, the more career breaks they are likely to have had.

Do different ethnic minority groups take more or fewer breaks than their white peers? Table 10.8 does not show any obvious differences in terms of number of breaks taken between the groups. Not only were career breaks not related to being held back, but, in addition, they did not vary by ethnicity.

Table 10.8 Number of career breaks since started nursing by ethnic origin

Percentages

Number of breaks	White	Black	Asian	Other	Not stated
0	44	41	48	42	48
1	29	27	25	28	26
2	18	20	18	19	18
3-9	9	12	9	11	8
10+	<1	1	<1	0	<1
Total nursing staff	11,968	608	344	222	1,054

134 nursing staff members did not answer the question

The comparisons made so far suggest several key factors that were related to position in the nursing grading scale. These include time in the nursing professions and various qualifications. In order to tie these factors together with the individual characteristics that the nursing and midwifery staff brought to their jobs (such as age and sex), the next stage will develop a multivariate model to predict nursing grade taking all these factors into account.

Predicting nursing grade: multivariate statistical analyses
It is too much to untangle the overall contribution of any one factor such as age to the grading situation of nursing and midwifery staff by simply using cross-sectional comparisons. In order to sort out whether any individual factor has an independent effect on progress in the profession (as measured by grade at time of the study), this next section introduces multivariate statistical analyses which predict nursing grade on the basis of factors such as age, length in the profession, and specialty. In multivariate statistics, the outcome variable (for example, nursing grade) is termed the *dependent variable*, and the predicting factors (for example, age and qualifications) are the *independent variables.*

The process used is called logistic regression. Similar to a multiple regression technique, logistic regression is used to predict a dichotomous variable (an 'either/or' outcome) rather than a continuous variable (ranging from a very low score to a very high score). Thus, it is particularly appropriate in these circumstances where we want to predict the probability of a nurse having reached a certain crucial grade or not.

Table 10.9 Predicting nursing grade: hypotheses

Personal characteristics

That certain personal characteristics will be related to the stage in the nursing grading scale reached, particularly:

1. That male nursing staff will have reached a higher point, other factors being held constant.

2. That age will be positively related to grade level.

3. That general educational level will be positively related to grade level.

Nursing career factors

That certain career factors will be related to the stage in the nursing grade scale reached, particularly:

4. That the longer a nursing staff member has been in the profession, the higher their grade.

5. That the higher their level of nursing qualification reached, the higher their grade.

6. That career breaks will not hold staff back from reaching the higher grades.

Features of the type of work being done

That certain features of their current job will be related to the stage in the nursing grade scale reached, particularly:

7. That working full-time is more likely to be associated with higher grades.

8. That staff working in certain, more unpopular and less academic specialties will be more likely to reach higher grades than their equivalents in the more popular and academic specialties.

The version used was that to be found in a statistical software package for the social sciences called SPSSX. For a fuller presentation of technical aspects of the analyses, see Appendix 4.

It was important that we did not use nursing grade as a continuous variable, but instead broke the grades up into a series of 'either/or' variables (for example, either grade C or above, or not; either Grade D or above, or not). Staff members were not evenly distributed across the grades, and there were several places in the grading system where the jump from one grade to the next meant more than the jump between two other grades. Thus, the jump from grade B to Grade C is very significant, indicating the difference between unqualified and qualified nursing and midwifery staff. The difference between C and D is rather different again, as most nurses with pre-Project 2000 training entered grade C if they were enrolled, and D if they were RGNs.

Thus, a set of models were run to predict the probability of staff members reaching any given grade level. The models were designed to test a series of hypotheses, derived from the previous cross-sectional results, from the qualitative case study work with the six nurse employers and from information based on previous reports.

To test these hypotheses, a set of six models was run. The first was to predict whether nurses had reached grade C or above, and included all qualified and unqualified staff. The subsequent five models were confined to qualified staff, and predicted whether they had reached grade D or above, grade E or above, grade F or above, grade G or above or, finally, grade H or above. Each model investigated which factors were the most important in predicting grade. Thus, for example, did a nurse's level of general education predict whether or not they reached grade C or above? Does it predict whether they will be a manager or not?

Two types of factors were used in the analyses as potential predictors of achievement of each grade. The first were continuous variables, such as age, length of time in the nursing professions, and general education score. The second type were categorical variables, such as which specialty the staff member worked in, or whether they were in full or part-time work. All the variables were coded as they were for the descriptive analyses presented in the previous chapters. The variables are summarised and presented in Table 10.10.

Table 10.10 Variables included in the multivariate analyses

Variable type	Number	Label	Description
Continuous	1	Age	
	2	Time in	Time in the nursing profession
	3	Quals	Nursing qualifications score
	4	Educate	General education score
Categorical	1	Sex	
	2	Worktype	Full or part-time work
	3	Sector	Specialty worked in
	4	Ethnicity	
	5	Breaks	Any career breaks taken

Predicting nursing grade: general results

We started with a series of models predicting nursing grade, *taking no account of ethnicity*. The other eight variables were entered into the equation in order of statistical significance. That is, the variables that contributed the most to predicting whether a staff member had reached a certain grade or not were entered first. Other variables were then entered in descending order of significance until only non-significant predictors were excluded. At each stage, the significance of a variable in contributing to the prediction was assessed once all the factors already in the equation were held constant.

Table 10.11 presents a summary of the significant variables included in each of the final models. Full details of the results from the analyses can be found in Appendix 4.

For all the six models, the length of time the nurse had spent in the profession, the level of nursing qualifications they had, and the specialty they worked in all retained some ability to predict the nursing grade level they had reached, when all other factors were held constant. The more qualifications they had, the more likely they were to be at a higher level in the grade structure – this was true at every step in the hierarchy. For qualified staff, the longer they had been in the profession, the more likely they were to be at a higher grade.

The relationship with the nursing specialty in which they worked was a little more complicated. From grade E upwards, all the way to the top at grade H, nursing staff in the medical specialties were less likely to have reached the higher grades. Nursing staff in the areas with traditionally lower status such as learning difficulties and the elderly were more likely to have higher grade posts. So too were nursing staff in midwifery and primary health care. The explanation for the higher grades associated with the last two might be that nursing and midwifery staff are more likely to be required to have post-basic qualifications in order to go into these fields in the first place, or that most newly qualified midwives are graded E or above on the basis of their direct care responsibilities. This is not the case with the 'lower status' specialties such as working with the elderly. In these cases, it is possible that it may be easier to reach a higher grade because there is less competition in these less popular specialties. This is important when we consider the earlier finding that the ethnic minority nursing staff were more likely to be in these less popular areas. Between 41 and 45 per cent of the ethnic minority nursing staff were working in mental illness, those with learning difficulties, and the elderly, compared to 24 per cent of the white staff.

Table 10.11 The influence of various factors on the probability of having reached various grades (in order of contribution)

Variable

Model 1: Reached grade C or above

Quals	(Prob. increased with more nursing qualifications)
Time in	(Prob. increased with longer time in nursing)
Age	(Prob. decreased if older)
Sector	(Prob. decreased by being in midwifery, compared to medical)

Model 2: Reached grade D or above

Quals	(Prob. increased with more nursing qualifications)
Sector	(Prob. increased by being in lower status or primary HC, prob. decreased by being in midwifery)
Time in	(Prob. increased with longer time in nursing)
Sex	(Prob. increased if male)

Model 3: Reached grade E or above

Quals	(Prob. increased with more nursing qualifications)
Time in	(Prob. increased with longer time in nursing)
Sector	(Prob. increased by being in lower status, primary HC or midwifery, compared to medical)
Educate	(Prob. increased with higher level of general education)
Age	(Prob. increased if older)

Model 4: Reached grade F or above

Quals	(Prob. increased with more nursing qualifications)
Sector	(Prob. increased by being in lower status, primary HC or midwifery, compared to medical)
Time in	(Prob. increased with longer time in nursing)
Worktype	(Prob. decreased if part-time)
Educate	(Prob. increased with higher level of general education)
Age	(Prob. increased if older)
Sex	(Prob. increased if male)

Model 5: Reached grade G or above

Sector	(Prob. increased by being in lower status or primary HC)
Quals	(Prob. increased with more nursing qualifications)
Time in	(Prob. increased with longer time in nursing)
Worktype	(Prob. decreased if part-time)
Educate	(Prob. increased with higher level of general education)
Age	(Prob. increased if older)
Sex	(Prob. increased if male)

Model 6: Reached grade H or above

Time in	(Prob. increased with longer time in nursing)
Educate	(Prob. increased with higher level of general education)
Worktype	(Prob. decreased if part-time)
Quals	(Prob. increased with more nursing qualifications)
Sector	(Prob. increased by being in lower status, primary HC or midwifery, compared to medical)
Age	(Prob. increased if older)
Sex	(Prob. increased if male)

Model 1 is based on all staff. Models 2 to 6 exclude unqualified staff.

At the lower end of the scale the relationship between specialty and grade was less clear. Unqualified nursing staff were *more* likely to be working in midwifery related specialties. Given the results presented above for the higher grades, it would seem that both the least and the most qualified nurses seemed to be in these areas, once all other factors were held constant. At grade D, the relationship was most unclear. When predicting which nurses would be D and above, being in the lower status specialties or primary health care increased the probability of having reached D or higher, whereas being in midwifery reduced the probability.

The relationship between specialty and progress is obviously a complicated one. All that we can conclude at this stage is that specialty is important in understanding nursing grades and career progress, and since the ethnic minorities are unevenly distributed across the nursing specialties, further work is needed to untangle how this either helps or hinders their progress.

In addition to these three main factors (time in the profession; level of nursing qualifications; specialty) there were other independent variables that were useful in predicting the different grade levels. Returning to each of the models in turn, obviously, whether or not staff members had nursing qualifications was the main factor predicting whether they were in the lowest, unqualified grades or not (Model 1). Some nurses with qualifications were doing posts for unqualified workers, but not very many. Beyond this main factor, general education, sex and whether or not they worked part-time were not important. After this point, unqualified staff members were excluded from the models.

Predicting whether or not nurses were at grade D or above (Model 2) was helped by knowing whether the nurses were male. This then remained important in predicting most of the higher grades in the subsequent models. Male nurses tended to be at higher grades. However, age, general education, and whether or not the nurses were working part-time did not help predict whether nurses were likely to have reached D or above.

The factors that were significant in predicting whether nurses were at grades E, F , G & H (Models 3, 4, 5 and 6) were all very similar. At each point, length of service in the profession, level of nursing qualifications, and specialty were all important. But level of general education was significant in its own right. Working part-time reduced the probability of reaching grades F or G. Generally, full-time workers with above average general educational qualifications were likely to be at the higher grades, even after all other factors were held constant.

It is interesting that age had a significant effect on the probability of reaching higher grades, *independently* of length of service. This means that of two nurses who each had (say) ten years accumulated service, the older one was more likely to be found in the higher grade. This might mean the 'life-experience' affects a nurse's ability to manage other staff; or it might mean that selection committees are instinctively biased towards maturer candidates. Either way, age was less important than length of service.

Within the qualified staff from grades C to H, at no point did the number of career breaks taken seem to be related to grade level in any way.

Despite the fact that they are built on cross-sectional data, rather than looking at change over time, this set of models begins to build a picture of the factors that might be important in progress in nursing. These analyses suggest that whether or not nurses reach the highest levels seems to be related to personal characteristics, nursing career factors, and features of the type of work being done. Since we already know that many of these vary according to which ethnic group nursing and midwifery staff belong to, it is important to control for them in the next step, which is to see whether their ethnic group membership had any additional relationship with their grade level.

Predicting nursing grade: the role of ethnicity in a general model of nursing progress

In the previous chapter, comparisons between the different minority groups highlighted some similarities and some differences, but the overall pattern was a little muddled. From the cross-sectional comparisons of grading level, we have evidence that at least some of the ethnic minority nursing and midwifery staff were reaching the heights of their profession in the same proportions as the white staff members, suggesting a fairly positive picture.

However, the cross-sectional analyses also suggested that the ethnic minority nursing and midwifery staff, in particular the black staff, were older, had been in the profession longer, and were more likely to be working full-time. All these things suggest that many of them should possibly be in *higher* grades than their white peers. On the other hand, we have seen that the ethnic minority staff members were less well qualified. On its own, this fact might lead us to think that they should be in *lower* grades than their white peers. Finally, there seems to be a tendency for ethnic minority nursing and midwifery staff to be concentrated in certain specialties, particularly the ones that might be thought of as less popular and less academic. The results from the previous section suggested that all these factors were important in some way in predicting nursing grade level.

The final set of logistic regression models, therefore, tested the hypothesis that membership of different ethnic minority groups made a significant additional contribution to grade, even when these other factors that have been identified as significant predictors of nursing grade are taken into account. It should be noted that there will be other, unmeasured, factors that are related to nursing grade, which were not included in the study, such as, for example, whether the nurse was ambitious to be promoted, or preferred to remain in 'real' nursing in close contact with patients. However, despite the fact that it cannot include all the relevant factors, this model provides some test for the presence of disadvantage (due to ethnic minority status) in the NHS grading system, after controlling for any earlier disadvantage that may have resulted in lower levels of general education, and lower levels of nursing qualifications. If, even when all personal characteristics and all nursing career characteristics, and all features of the working situation are controlled for, there is still evidence that ethnicity predicts grade level, then it becomes a possibility that ethnic minority nurses are facing direct discrimination in their workplaces, or that there are other factors related to being a member of particular ethnic minority groups which are having an effect.

The same set of six models were run again, excluding the variable 'career breaks', since this had been found in the previous section to be unrelated to grade level. All factors that were related to grade level at some point were retained. In addition, the five-way classification of ethnic group (white, black, Asian, Other and Not Stated) was added to each model. The results are summarised in Table 10.12. Again, the details are in Appendix 4.

At the very bottom and the very top of the grading structure, ethnic group membership was not a valuable predictor. Thus, where we were seeking to predict which nursing and midwifery staff members were at grade C or above only, whether or not staff members were unqualified was unrelated to their ethnic group membership[1]. At the top, whether or not nursing and midwifery staff were grade H or above was not significantly related to their ethnicity.

However, when predicting whether nurses were grade F or above, and grade G or above, there was a significant statistical effect for being a black nurse, even when all other significant predictors of nursing grade were controlled for. Black nurses were at a disadvantage when compared

179

Table 10.12 The influence of ethnicity on the probability of having reached various grades, after controlling for other significant predictors

Model 1: Reached grade C or above
After controlling for qualifications, time in the nursing profession, age and sector worked in: Ethnicity not significant

Model 2: Reached grade D or above
After controlling for qualifications, sector worked in, time in the nursing professions and sex: Ethnicity not significant

Model 3: Reached grade E or above
After controlling for qualifications, time in the nursing professions, sector, general educational level and age: Asians and 'Other' ethnic minorities have a higher probability of reaching grade E or above compared with white staff.

Model 4: Reached grade F or above
After controlling for qualifications, sector worked in, time in the nursing professions, work type, general educational level, age and sex: Black staff have a lower probability of having reached grade F or above compared with white staff. Asians appear also to have a slightly lower probability, but the difference is not significant.

Model 5: Reached grade G or above
After controlling for sector worked in, qualifications, time in the nursing professions, work type, education, age and sex: Black staff have a lower probability of having reached grade F or above compared with white staff. Asians appear also to have a slightly lower probability, but the difference is not significant.

Model 6: Reached grade H or above
After controlling for time in the nursing professions, general educational level, work type, qualifications, sector worked in, age and sex: Ethnicity not significant, though the indications are in the direction of the minorities having a slightly lower chance of reaching these senior posts.

**Figure 10.3 Summary of the logistic regression results: the effect of
ethnicity on predictions of nursing grade**

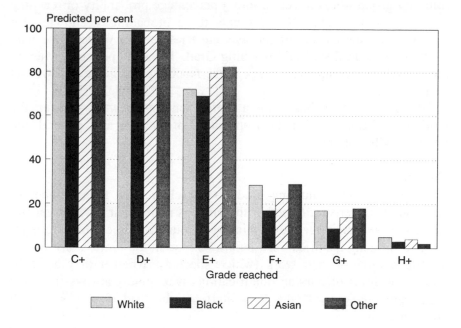

to their white peers, and to staff members from other ethnic groups.
However, being of Asian origin, or of the mixed other group, did not
have a significant effect on nursing grade when the other significant
factors were held constant.

In model 3, however, predicting whether nurses would have reached
grade E or above, slightly fewer black nurses would be predicted to have
reached the grade than whites, but significantly *more* Asians and those in
the 'Other' category would be predicted to have reached that grade.

In order to clarify these results, the probability of a member of each
of the ethnic group reaching the different nursing grades was calculated,
relative to the probability that a white nurse, identical in all other respects
(sex, age, length of time in profession etc) would also reach that grade.
The calculations were based on a 'reference' qualified nurse who was
female, working full-time, 39 years old, of average general education, of
average time in the nursing profession, and who had an average number
of points on the nursing qualification scale. Calculations were based on
nursing staff working in the medical specialties. The only difference
between the nurses was their ethnic group.

The logistic regression procedure outputs odds-ratios. The notion of an odds-ratio is a little difficult to grasp, and so in these results the changes in odds-ratio estimates associated with being in a certain ethnic minority group were converted into a percentage probability of reaching a certain grade. Figure 10.3 presents these probabilities, showing for example that the chance of the average ('reference') white nurse who works in a medical specialty reaching Grade F was 29 per cent, whereas the chance of a comparable black nurse reaching that grade is lower, at 18 per cent.

Predictions were based on a 'reference' nurse who was female, working full-time in a medical specialty, of average age, general and nursing qualifications.

Conclusion

In general, a higher nursing grade is closely related to a number of personal characteristics (whether the nurse is male, their level of general education, and their age); to a number of nursing career characteristics (level of nursing qualifications, length of time in the profession); and to certain features of their work (which specialty, whether they are full-time). The level of nursing qualifications was almost always the most significant predictor of whether a staff member had reached a certain grade or higher.

It is important that we get a clear picture of what effect ethnicity had on people's grades. Up to and including grade E, members of ethnic minority groups were not at a disadvantage at all. Indeed, Asians were doing rather better at grade E than other nurses with similar levels of qualifications and experience.

However, when we turn to the senior grades, the models show that:

- Black nurses fell significantly behind white nurses of similar qualifications and experience in the competition to reach grades F and G. The model suggests that the same may have been true at the most senior level (grade H and above) but we cannot be confident that this result did not arise by chance;

- For Asian nurses, the proportion of the sample reaching each of the higher level grades (F, G or H and above) was slightly lower than for whites, but, again, we cannot be confident that this is true of all nurses.

Even in the models where ethnicity was most important, it was much less effective in explaining the overall pattern of grades than most of the other variables, especially qualifications, length of service and specialty.

To the extent that some of these more powerful variables are indications of skills and experience (education, qualifications and length of service), promotion is seen to be meritocratic. To the extent that variables are implicated which do not indicate ability to perform the job (sector, part-time work, sex, age and ethnicity) the system appears to be capricious. The fact that ethnicity does not appear in all models, and is a relatively weak predictor where it does appear, is heartening.

On the other hand, black and Asian nursing and midwifery staff represent only a small proportion of the whole sample, and a variable which has only a weak effect on the *overall* pattern can still have a big influence on the outcome *for small groups*. A black nurse faced an obstacle in moving from grade E to grade F equivalent to seven years of experience (all other things being equal). That is not to be dismissed lightly.

This statistical model cannot pin down the exact reason for the lower level of achievement by black nurses and it is possible to think of several explanations for the difference apart from discrimination. One hypothesis might be that black nurses were less career orientated than their white counterparts (perhaps because they have been demotivated by the experience of discrimination in the past); if so, they may not have applied for senior posts. We did not specifically investigate that possibility, and cannot prove or disprove it, though lack of motivation was not specially noticeable among the black nurses interviewed for the case histories. Another hypothesis is that they did apply for higher grades, but faced adverse and unfair discrimination at the selection stage. These hypotheses need testing in further research studies. Discrimination has not been investigated directly, but the results suggest that it could be at work. Discrimination is illegal, even if the people making biased judgements were not conscious of their prejudice. The primary value of the research is in pointing clearly to the group most likely to have been affected by discrimination: black nursing and midwifery staff looking for advancement above grade E.

These issues all require further analyses and these results should not be taken as definitive. The greatest value of these analyses is in their suggestion of the complexity of the issue. More sophisticated models of career progression and of discrimination need to be developed in order to lead to better understanding of the processes underlying progress of ethnic minorities in NHS nursing. In particular, longitudinal data would help to untangle some of the underlying processes. The data on which these analyses were based were cross-sectional, and thus necessarily limited in terms of inferences about progress over time.

The next part of the report takes a step back from these progress analyses, and looks in more detail at the ways that nursing staff see their opportunities within their jobs, and at how they feel generally about their work as NHS staff members.

Note
1. In predicting grade C or above, members of the group who refused to state their ethnicity were in fact significantly less likely to be qualified than white staff. Since nothing is known about their ethnicity, we cannot draw any conclusions from this.

11 Training opportunities

The previous section showed that there were ethnic minority differences in grading, in that the nursing grade of certain ethnic minority nursing and midwifery staff was lower than an equivalent white staff member who resembled them in every other respect. The results were especially significant in suggesting that the effects of ethnicity were clearest for black staff members, but that in the analyses undertaken for this study, there was not a significant relationship between being from another ethnic minority group and nursing grade level.

What was not clear from the analyses was the form that the discrimination against black nursing and midwifery staff takes. Within the bounds of this postal survey, it is not possible to investigate the mechanisms by which any discrimination is being made manifest in practice, as the survey only contains the reports of the nursing and midwifery staff themselves and cannot analyse the staff members in interaction with their employer and general working environment. In addition, the previous analyses have all been based on 'facts' about the nursing and midwifery staff lives and grades. Of further interest is the ways in which staff members from different ethnic backgrounds feel discriminated against in different ways, regardless of its 'factual' basis. This and the subsequent chapter will present nursing and midwifery staff impressions of discrimination in terms of their access to training opportunities and flexible working, and will investigate differences in the attitudes of various groups of nursing and midwifery staff to their work within the NHS.

Conversion courses and post-basic training

Unqualified staff
One quarter of the unqualified staff members in the study had applied for basic-nurse training, indicating that many of those doing basic auxiliary work were interested in it as an avenue into qualified nursing. Presumably there may have been more unqualified and auxiliary staff who will

be interested in applying at a slightly later stage, or who were interested but not confident enough to do so at the point when they took part in the PSI survey. A slightly smaller proportion, approximately one fifth of all unqualified staff, had completed an National Vocational Qualification (NVQ), and just less than a fifth were currently studying for an NVQ.

Table 11.1 shows that there were few differences between the ethnic groups in terms of their applications for nurse training or their participation in NVQ courses. Slightly more of the ethnic minority nursing staff had applied for the basic training, but equal proportions were participating in NVQ training. Although presenting percentages makes comparison between the groups much easier, it should be noted that as numbers of unqualified staff in the study as a whole were quite low, splitting the unqualified groups up reduces the numbers available for analysis quite considerably.

Table 11.1 Unqualified staff: participation in training

Percentages

Participation in training	White	Black	Asian	Other	Not stated
Applied for basic nurse training	22	34	33	33	23
Completed NVQ training	22	16	26	18	14
Currently NVQ training	19	19	22	13	14
Total nursing staff	2,412	141	45	25	251

Approximately 10 per cent of unqualified nursing staff did not answer these questions.

Unqualified staff members either felt encouraged to participate in training (36 per cent), or they felt that the management was neutral but not actively discouraging (56 per cent). Only a very small group (8 per cent) felt actively discouraged. There were virtually no differences between the ethnic groups in terms of encouragement felt, as Table 11.2 shows.

Table 11.2 Unqualified staff: felt encouraged to take part in training by ethnic group

Percentages

Level of encouragement	White	Black	Asian	Other	Not stated
Encouraged	36	38	36	36	36
Neither encouraged nor discouraged	56	54	62	52	53
Discouraged	8	8	2	12	11
Total nursing staff	2,582	163	49	27	276

Approximately 10 per cent of unqualified nursing staff did not answer these questions.

Qualified staff

One of the most significant questions in relation to training for already qualified nurses has been the ease of access to conversion courses for nurses who entered the profession as enrolled but who then wished to convert to being registered. With the introduction of Project 2000, whereby all nurses now enter the profession at the same level, this is less of an issue. However, it still remains a significant matter for nurses who have been in the profession for more than four years, as most of the nurses in this survey had been.

Looking only at enrolled staff in the survey, it appeared that 49 per cent had applied for conversion courses at some point. Table 11.3 shows that the rate was approximately equal across the various ethnic minority groups, being between 46 and 48 per cent for all groups except the Asian group, where 62 per cent had applied for conversion courses. Success in getting onto a conversion course varied a little between the groups, however, and here the white group were most successful. Another significant issue with respect to conversion courses was whether or not the nurse employer seconded the nurse to the course, and here the numbers are rather small for comparison. The majority of nurses who get onto conversion courses would appear to be seconded by their employers.

Overall, enrolled nurses felt that management was either encouraging (34 per cent) or neutral (56 per cent) about their participation in conversion courses. Only a small minority (10 per cent) felt actively discouraged. The extent to which members of the different ethnic groups felt actively discouraged varied a little, with least discouragement felt by the white and black nurses and midwifery staff (10 per cent and 11 per

Table 11.3 Conversion courses for enrolled nurses

Percentages

Participation in training	White	Black	Asian	Other	Not stated
Applied for conversion course	48	46	62	47	46
Of those who applied: Succeeded in obtaining a place	54	35	44	34	35
Of those who had a place: Seconded by employer	88	100	77	90	81
Total nursing staff	1,902				

157 of enrolled nurses did not answer the conversion course questions

cent respectively) and most felt by the Asians and the 'Other' group (17 per cent and 19 per cent respectively). The multivariate analyses in the previous section suggested that the chances of Asian nurses reaching the higher grades was better than that of the black staff. As mentioned then, it is possible that the discrimination exists, but is then negotiated in some way by the Asian staff, so that on objective comparisons they seem to be free from the effects of discrimination.

In addition to conversion courses for enrolled nurses, all qualified nurses, enrolled and registered, can also go on to study for post-basic qualifications. We looked at rates of completion of these post-basic courses, and found that approximately half of all qualified nurses had completed such courses at the time the survey was undertaken. The rates were lowest for the Asians (44 per cent) and highest for the group who did not specify their ethnicity (55 per cent), with the other groups ranged in between. White and black staff reported almost identical rates of completion (51 per cent and 52 per cent respectively). On the basis of these figures, there would seem to be little evidence of discrimination in access to post-basic training courses. In addition to those who had completed such courses, approximately 12 per cent of the qualified nurses were currently registered on such courses, and again these figures were very similar across the ethnic groups, ranging between 9 per cent for the 'Other' group to 13 per cent for the 'Not stated' group.

Turning finally to encouragement for post-basic course participation by qualified nurses, again low rates of active discouragement were reported, reflecting the results for both encouragement for basic training amongst the unqualified, and encouragement for conversion course training amongst the enrolled. Only 13 per cent of the qualified nursing and midwifery staff felt discouraged, and this rate was very similar across the groups ranging from 10 to 15 per cent, with the white group reporting slightly more active discouragement than the black or Asian groups.

Access to information about courses

Unqualified staff
One third (34 per cent) of all unqualified staff reported that getting information about relevant courses was easy, and a further 23 per cent reported that it was neither easy nor difficult. A high proportion, 43 per cent of unqualified staff, said that it was difficult to get such information. Again, a word of reservation is warranted concerning presentation of percentages for the small numbers of unqualified staff in the study, and given the size of the groups, Table 11.4 suggests that there was little difference in terms of access to information between the groups.

Table 11.4   Access to training information reported by unqualified staff

					Percentages
Access to information	White	Black	Asian	Other	Not stated
Easy access	35	23	29	29	32
Neutral	23	30	20	36	22
Difficult access	42	47	51	35	46
Total unqualified staff	2,412	141	45	25	251

Qualified staff
Overall, qualified staff suggested that access to information regarding training was easier for them than it was for the unqualified staff. Over half of the qualified staff reported that they had easy access to the relevant training information, and 18 per cent reported that access was 'neither easy nor difficult'. Approximately a quarter of qualified staff reported that getting the right information was difficult.

Again, little variation was seen between the different ethnicities when the figures were analysed by ethnic group. These are presented in Table

Table 11.5 Access to training information reported by qualified staff

Percentages

Access to information	White	Black	Asian	Other	Not stated
Easy access	55	51	45	54	55
Neutral	17	18	25	23	18
Difficult access	28	30	30	22	27
Total qualified staff	9,131	431	287	192	724

11.5, which shows that very similar proportions of qualified nurses in all the groups reported that access was difficult.

In conclusion, access to information about training courses was more difficult than it should have been for a substantial proportion of both qualified and unqualified nurses, and difficulty was experienced more by the latter than the former. However, against this background, there was little evidence for any active discrimination against members of ethnic minority groups, in that reports of access to information did not vary much between the groups.

Time-off for courses
Whether or not paid time-off is provided by employers for training courses is likely to be a significant factor in uptake of courses. Overall, nurses reported that it was difficult for them to get paid leave to study.

Unqualified staff
Unqualified staff were fairly equally divided in their opinion of whether getting paid time-off was easy (34 per cent) or difficult (40 per cent). The remainder (26 per cent) felt it was neither easy nor difficult.

Table 11.6 shows that within this overall pattern there was little variation reported by different ethnic groups. The group reporting that it was most difficult was black nursing staff, who reported the lowest rate of easy access (26 per cent) and the highest rate of difficulty (42 per cent). However, the differences were not very large, nor were they significant, and the group reporting the second highest level of difficulty was the white group (40 per cent).

Table 11.6 Paid time-off for training courses: unqualified staff

Percentages

Ease of access to paid time-off	White	Black	Asian	Other	Not stated
Easy access	34	26	32	43	37
Neutral	26	32	32	26	24
Difficult access	40	42	36	31	39
Total unqualified staff	2,294	123	419	230	234

Qualified staff

Over half of qualified nursing and midwifery staff (57 per cent) reported that it was difficult to get employers to pay for time to attend courses. Of the remainder, 16 per cent felt that it was neither easy nor difficult, and 27 per cent that it was easy.

Again, little variation is seen between the ethnic groups and there was no evidence of discrimination. Table 11.7 shows that the numbers of qualified staff reporting difficulties ranged between 47 and 58 per cent, with the highest level of reports of difficulties coming from the white group.

Table 11.7 Paid time-off for training courses: qualified staff

Percentages

Ease of access to paid time-off	White	Black	Asian	Other	Not stated
Easy access	27	28	28	28	28
Neutral	16	22	20	25	16
Difficult access	58	58	52	47	56
Total qualified staff	9,113	429	289	190	725

In conclusion, nursing staff reports suggested that it was slightly easier for unqualified staff to get paid time-off for courses than it was for the qualified staff. In both cases, it was relatively hard. However, rates did not vary significantly between the various ethnic groups and it does not seem to be the case that discrimination is active within the granting of paid time-off for further study.

Fee-payment for training courses and general encouragement by management

Of all the aspects of training, having employers who paid course fees was the issue that resulted in this highest level of difficulty reported. There is no expectation that unqualified and auxiliary staff will do training courses, so fee payment is not a major issue from the perspective of the employer. However, qualified nursing and midwifery staff are expected to keep up their training in order to continue with their registration, and the role of employers in paying fees is thus very significant.

Qualified staff

Nearly two-thirds (61 per cent) of qualified staff reported that it was difficult to get employers to fund courses. Less than a quarter (21 per cent) found it easy. Table 11.8 shows that again, there were few differences between the ethnic minority groups in this respect, and, if anything, the white group reported higher levels of difficulty.

Table 11.8 Course fee payments by employers

Percentages

Ease of getting employer to pay	White	Black	Asian	Other	Not stated
Easy	21	21	19	19	23
Neither easy nor difficult	17	24	24	28	15
Difficult	62	56	57	53	62
Total qualified staff	9,113	429	289	190	725

Conclusion

Information about courses is available to staff, and many manage to register for some form of further nursing qualification, be it basic nurse training, a conversion course, or post-basic training. However, difficulties arise in getting employers to provide paid time-off, and to contribute to course fees.

The relatively large numbers of unqualified staff who felt encouraged to take part in training was an unexpected result, as there are few courses open to them apart from in-house refresher courses. However, National Vocational Training Qualifications are being widely developed and are expected to become the official training structure for unqualified staff. Chapter 5 refers to these issues in further detail.

Within this broad picture of training opportunities for nursing and midwifery staff, there were few differences between the ethnic minority groups who reported very similar levels of ease and difficulty with respect to the different aspects of acquiring further training. These results confirm the results from the case studies of nurse employers in the earlier chapter, where the problem seemed to be one of training opportunities and career structure for nursing and midwifery staff as a whole. In the face of a changing NHS, and restricted resources, the issue will become crucial as more decisions have to be made about how the increasingly limited opportunities are allocated. Despite the fact that discrimination in training opportunities did not appear to be a major issue of concern for nursing and midwifery staff at the time of this survey, the case studies in the earlier chapter suggested that without clearer equal opportunity practices, the chances of discriminatory behaviour might be a possibility.

12 Perceptions and attitudes of nursing and midwifery staff in the NHS

Previous chapters have demonstrated that being a black nurse or midwife in the NHS is a disadvantage in terms of reaching the higher nursing grades. However, the source of these variations between ethnic groups is not obvious, and differences did not show up in terms of access to training. The final two chapters will look more closely at the perceptions and feelings of the nursing and midwifery staff generally, and the quality of their relationships with their colleagues and patients, and will examine whether there are any differences in terms of the ways in which the various ethnic groups describe their work in the NHS.

Feelings about current grade and working conditions

Once having entered nursing and reached the grade at which they were when the survey took place, nursing and midwifery staff are likely to have varying thoughts about the nature of their work, and aspects of the grading structure as it applies to them. These feelings about aspects of their current grade and their working conditions are likely to colour their overall feelings about the nursing professions and may be part of their experience of discrimination.

Staff members were asked about a number of aspects of their current job, including whether the work could have been undertaken by staff of a higher or lower grade than themselves; the extent of extended managerial roles they have to play; whether their current grade is fair; and any appeals against grading that they might have made.

Staff members were asked whether the work they did should be undertaken by staff of a lower or higher grade than themselves. The proportions of nursing and midwifery staff from each of the groups who felt that this was so on a daily or weekly basis are shown in Tables 12.1 and 12.2.

Tables 12.1 and 12.2 suggest that two-thirds of the staff members felt that aspects of their job could be lower grade, and over half also felt that aspects could be higher grade. In both cases, the proportions of ethnic

194

**Table 12.1   In your opinion, do you do work which should be
undertaken by a lower grade of staff?**

Percentages

Ethnic origin	Undertakes work which could be lower grade daily or weekly
White	59
Black	68
Asian	67
Other	67
Not stated	56
Total nursing staff	13,836

494 nursing staff members did not answer the question.

**Table 12.2   In your opinion, do you do work which should be
undertaken by a higher grade of staff?**

Percentages

Ethnic origin	Undertakes work which could be higher grade daily or weekly
White	52
Black	60
Asian	59
Other	57
Not stated	51
Total nursing staff	13,903

427 nursing staff members did not answer the question.

minority nurses who felt this to be the case was higher than the
proportion of whites feeling so.

Table 12.3 suggests that although two-thirds felt their job could be
higher grade, rather fewer felt that they were doing an extended role in
their grade, or taking on extended management responsibilities.
Significantly more Asian and Other nursing staff felt they were taking on
an extended role in their current post. In addition to these two groups,

Table 12.3 Aspects of current job: extended role or management responsibilities in current job?

Percentages

Question	Answering 'Yes'				
	White	Black	Asian	Other	Not stated
Extended role in current job?	39.7	41.2	48.3	53.6	33.5
Other management responsibilities?	22.4	27.1	39.8	41.7	20.5

black nursing staff were also significantly more likely than white nursing staff and nursing staff who had not stated their ethnicity to have taken on other management responsibilities.

The suggestion that perhaps nursing and midwifery staff simply feel that their grade is not 'right' in some way, is reflected in the next table, which shows the percentage of nursing staff from each of the ethnic minority groups who believed that their current grade was not a fair reflection of what they did. The lower rate of black nursing and midwifery staff who felt that their grade was unfair was interesting, bearing in mind that the multivariate analyses had suggested that their grades were possibly *more* unfair.

Table 12.4 Do you think your current grade is a fair reflection of the duties and responsibilities you have at work?

Percentages

Ethnic origin	Current grade considered unfair
White	58
Black	42
Asian	50
Other	62
Not stated	54
Total nursing staff	14,176

1 per cent of nursing staff did not answer the question.

All nursing and midwifery staff in the NHS in 1988 were part of the regrading exercise, when the current system of grading (from A to I) was introduced. They were entitled to appeal against their grade after the regrading. These relatively high rates of dissatisfaction with current grade reflected in the preceding tables would suggest that many nurses may have appealed against their grade. Indeed, Table 12.5, which presents grade appeal information for nurses who were in the NHS in 1988 only, shows that anything between a quarter and a half of the nursing and midwifery staff had appealed against their grade. Appeals were highest among two ethnic minority groups, the black group and the 'Other' group. Rates of appeal were lowest among the whites, the Asians and the 'Ethnicity not stated' groups.

Table 12.5 Have you appealed against your 1988 regrading?
(Nursing staff who were in the NHS in 1988 only)

Percentages

Ethnic origin	Appealed against 1988 regrading	Of those who appealed, successful
White	28	44
Black	35	32
Asian	29	33
Other	40	41
Not stated	29	30
Total nursing staff	10,475	2,867

3 per cent of nursing staff did not answer the first question and, of those, 5 per cent did not answer the second.

Appeals were more often unsuccessful than successful with less than half of all groups being regraded as a result. However, to some extent rates of success varied between the ethnic groups, with over ten per cent more of the white appeals being successful. Without more information about the nature of the initial grades and the substance of the appeal, it is difficult to conclude that this is the result of discrimination, and further research would be necessary to assess how far the initial grades in the 1988 regrading were unfair, and to what extent, if any, the appeal procedure was discriminatory.

General attitude to the job

Given these somewhat ambivalent feelings about their current grade, how satisfied are nursing and midwifery staff generally with their present post? Staff members were asked to rate each of 13 aspects of their work on a scale from 1 to 4, where 1 was 'very dissatisfied', 2 was 'dissatisfied', 3 was 'neither satisfied nor dissatisfied' and 4 was 'very satisfied'. Table 12.6 ranks the main areas of satisfaction in order, for all nursing and midwifery staff, with the area generating most satisfaction at the top of the table and the areas giving least satisfaction at the bottom.

Table 12.6   Satisfaction with the job: how satisfied are you with the following in your present post?

Percentages

	Nursing staff satisfied with each item
Relations with patients/clients	89
Relations with colleagues	81
Opportunity to work the hours you want	50
Amount of auxiliary support	38
Amount of qualified nurse support	38
Your involvement in decision-making	37
Your present workload	34
Your basic pay	32
Amount of training opportunities	32
Amount of time for clinical nursing duties	30
Your security of employment	29
Amount of administrative/clerical work	20
Your promotion prospects	20
Satisfaction overall	55
Total nursing staff	14,330

As the final line of the table shows, over half of the nursing and midwifery staff were satisfied overall with their work. The areas generating most satisfaction were their relationships with patients and colleagues, and the flexibility of the working hours. Security, amount of administration work and promotion prospects were bottom of the list.

Table 12.7 Are ethnic groups dissatisfied with different aspects of their jobs?

Percentages

Ethnic group	Areas generating most dissatisfaction (bottom five*)	Not wholly satisfied with this area*
White	Training opportunities	68
	Clinical time	70
	Job security	71
	Promotion prospects	80
	Amount of admin work	80
Black	Involvement in decisions	76
	Job security	79
	Amount of admin work	78
	Pay	82
	Promotion prospects	87
Asian	Auxiliary support	74
	Pay	79
	Amount of admin work	81
	Job security	84
	Promotion prospects	88
Other	Training opportunities	69) joint
	Clinical time	69)
	Involvement in decisions	70
	Job security	77
	Amount of admin work	82
	Promotion prospects	84
Ethnicity not stated	Workload	65) joint
	Security	65)
	Pay	67) joint
	Clinical time	67)
	Amount of admin work	76
	Promotion prospects	80
Total nursing staff		14,330

If two items received the same level of dissatisfaction rating, both are listed (as joint).

*   All except the 'don't know' category are percentages of those who stated an option.

Do these areas of satisfaction vary by ethnic group? The five areas with which nursing and midwifery staff were most dissatisfied were identified for each of the ethnic groups, and these are displayed in Table 12.7.

Basically, there were few notable variations among the groups. For most staff it was pay, security and promotion prospects that worried them the most, together with aspects of their job such as the amount of administration work involved.

Perceptions of the future

Finally, how does the NHS nursing and midwifery staff see its future at this time of extensive change and reorganisation in the NHS?

Table 12.8 lists the things that the nursing and midwifery staff expected to be doing in three years time. Overwhelmingly, staff members see their future within the NHS. Four-fifths of staff members thought that

Table 12.8 The future: what do you expect to be doing in three years from now?

Percentages

	Nursing staff rating each item*
Same nursing job as present	42
Better NHS nursing job than present	37
Raising a family	13
Full or part-time education	9
Non-nursing job	7
Retired	7
Redundant	7
Nursing job in the private sector	5
Lower grade than present	4
Unemployed	3
Nursing job overseas	3
Non-nursing job overseas	<1
Don't know	9
Other	2
Total nursing staff	14,330

*   Nursing staff could chose more than one item, hence the total percentage exceeds 100.

Table 12.9   Do ethnic groups have different perceptions of what they will be doing in three years?

Percentages

Ethnic group	Perceived situation in three years time (top five)	Naming this item*
White	Same job as present	43
	Better NHS job	37
	Raising family	14
	Education	9
	Don't know	8
Black	Better NHS job	41
	Same job as present	28
	Don't know	15
	Education	14
	Retired	12
Asian	Better NHS job	46
	Same job as present	26
	Don't know	16
	Education	11
	Non-nursing	9
Other	Better NHS job	42
	Same job as present	41
	Don't know	12
	Education	11
	Redundant	8
Ethnicity not stated	Same job as present	42
	Better NHS job	31
	Retired	14
	Raising family	10
	Don't know	7
Total nursing staff	14,330	

*   All except the 'don't know' category are percentages of those who stated an option.

they would either be doing the same job within the NHS, or a better job within the NHS. Despite their concern about job security, few actually thought that they would be unemployed or redundant in three years time. Approximately a quarter thought that they would be taking a career break of some kind, to raise children or study for further qualifications.

Other responses included, 'it depends on the Trust' (17), 'bank nursing' (10), 'conversion course' (8), 'travel' (8) and 'social services' (6).

Again, the different ethnic groups showed few variations in terms of their visions of the future. Table 12.9 lists the top five likely situations that nursing and midwifery staff thought they would be in in three years time, and for all groups this was a future with the NHS.

Conclusion

Aspects of their current job and their working conditions do cause worry and concern for NHS nursing and midwifery staff. In particular, they are not confident that their current grade is correct, and they are not satisfied with pay, job security or promotion prospects. However, overall they are more satisfied than dissatisfied, and, in addition, the areas of dissatisfaction and satisfaction do not vary noticeably by ethnic group. Despite concern over security and dissatisfaction with pay, the majority of all the nursing and midwifery staff in the study saw their future within the NHS.

13 Equal opportunities and race relations issues

In addition to the questions on training opportunities and general feelings about working as nursing and midwifery staff, the survey questionnaire asked respondents a range of direct questions on their attitudes towards equal opportunities and their beliefs about being discriminated against while working in the NHS. These included specific and general questions about equal opportunities and more detailed questions on beliefs about discrimination in the areas of recruitment, training and promotional opportunities. The views of nursing and midwifery staff specifically concerning discrimination form this last chapter of this report.

Chapter 8 documented the nature of racial harassment to which ethnic minority nurses and midwifery staff were subjected. These findings based on 114 interviews with white and ethnic minority staff suggest that:

- A large proportion of ethnic minority nursing staff had experienced racial harassment from patients and to a lesser extent from nursing colleagues and management;

- This racial harassment constituted a regular feature of working life for ethnic minority nursing staff;

- Very few white nursing staff reported being subjected to racial harassment from patients, nursing colleagues or management;

- Few incidents of racial harassment were reported to management because of the lack of confidence among ethnic minority staff in management being able to deal with it effectively.

Those were the qualitative findings which provide information about the nature of racial harassment and the relationships between harassed and harassers. This chapter will provide an assessment of the extent of racial harassment and discrimination that ethnic minority staff were subjected to.

Perceptions of racial discrimination in recruitment

The extent of racial discrimination in recruitment

Respondents were asked a number of questions regarding their beliefs on the extent of racial discrimination in recruitment: at a general level within the NHS, within their own workplace, and within their own careers. Their answers to these questions are displayed in Table 13.1. The first question asked if they felt that applicants are ever refused nursing jobs in the NHS for reasons to do with their 'race' or colour, and the first line of Table 13.1 suggests that most nursing staff believed that racial discrimination in recruitment existed in the NHS. There were large differences between groups, with much larger proportions of staff from ethnic minority groups believing that racial discrimination in recruitment existed, compared with white nursing staff and nursing staff who did not state their ethnic group. Throughout this section the answers of respondents who did not state their ethnic group closely mirrored the responses given by white nursing staff.

Table 13.1 Perceptions of racial discrimination in recruitment

	White	Black	Asian	Other	Not stated
Per cent believing *NHS jobs* are refused for ethnic reasons[1]	55	85	79	72	58
Per cent believing that *jobs in their workplace* are refused for ethnic reasons[2]	24	66	62	51	26
Per cent believing *they* have been refused jobs for ethnic reasons[3]	1	26	26	17	1

[1] Total nursing staff (538 did not respond to this question)   13,792
[2] Total nursing staff (914 did not respond to this question)   13,416
[3] Total nursing staff (402 did not respond to this question)   13,928

The second question asked whether they thought that applicants were ever refused jobs in their own workplace for reasons to do with ethnicity. The second line of Table 13.1 shows that a smaller proportion of all respondents believed that racial discrimination in recruitment occurred within their own workplace as compared to within the NHS overall. Once again, those from ethnic minorities were more likely to believe that this was going on: two-thirds of black and Asian staff compared with a quarter of white staff.

Finally, respondents were asked about their own personal experience. In particular whether they themselves had ever been refused a nursing job in the NHS for ethnic reasons. As the last line of Table 13.1 shows, the majority of all nursing staff regardless of ethnicity did not feel they had personally experienced discrimination in recruitment in the NHS. However, there were differences between ethnic groups. Over a quarter of black and Asian nursing staff and nearly a fifth of nursing staff from other ethnic minority groups believed they had been refused a job in the NHS for reasons to do with their 'race' or colour. In contrast only one per cent of nursing staff who did not state their ethnicity and one per cent of white nursing staff felt they had been discriminated against in this manner.

Our findings suggest that all groups of nursing staff members were more likely to feel that discrimination existed in recruitment in the NHS as a whole rather than within their own workplace, or in their own experience. This pattern of beliefs of these ethnic minority staff is similar to those of other ethnic minority workers as documented by Brown (1984).

Who is racially discriminated against in recruitment?

If they believed that recruitment discrimination existed within the NHS or within their workplace, we went on to ask respondents which groups, in their opinion, were most likely to be discriminated against. Respondents were given the choice of white nursing staff, black and Asian nursing staff, or both white and black and Asian nursing staff. We purposely grouped together black and Asian nursing staff as we were interested in documenting the extent to which respondents felt that 'colour' racism was taking place. However, we could not be sure how respondents had categorised those they considered as most likely to be discriminated against. For instance, we could not be sure that those labelled black or Asian by our respondents would themselves identify with these terms.

The results to these two questions are shown in Table 13.2. The table shows a clear divide between the groups. The first section shows that a large proportion of black staff members and over three fifths of Asian and other ethnic minority nursing staff believed that black or Asian nursing staff were most likely to be the targets of recruitment discrimination in the NHS. In comparison, a little over half of both white staff members and those who had not stated their ethnic group felt that

Table 13.2 Who is discriminated against?

	White	Black	Asian	Other	Not stated
In the NHS in general[1]					
Per cent believing that *white* staff are discriminated against	1	0	1	1	2
Per cent believing that *black and Asian* staff are discriminated against	45	74	65	64	45
Per cent believing *white, black and Asian* staff are discriminated against	54	25	34	35	53
In my workplace[2]					
Per cent believing that *white* staff are discriminated against	2	1	1	2	3
Per cent believing that *black and Asian* staff are discriminated against	47	73	66	62	46
Per cent believing *white, black and Asian* staff are discriminated against	51	26	33	36	51

[1] Total nursing staff (398 did not respond to this question)   7,549
[2] Total nursing staff (133 did not respond to this question)   3,509

both white and black and Asian nursing staff would be likely to experience recruitment discrimination in the NHS.

The second section of the table shows the same pattern. All the ethnic minority groups felt that black or Asian nurses were most likely to be discriminated against in recruitment at their workplaces. However, many white staff members thought that white staff faced discrimination as well as black or Asian staff. This interesting result may relate to earlier findings in Chapter 6 in which some white nursing staff perceived equal opportunities as a gender rather then an ethnic or 'race' issue. However, these proportions should be assessed in the light of the fact that far fewer white staff reported that there was any racial discrimination in their workplace in the first place (Table 13.1).

The qualitative interviews had suggested that a small number of white nursing staff felt 'cheated' by the introduction of equal opportunities policies at work. This was because they felt that the introduction of such policies had led to white nursing staff being discriminated against in favour of ethnic minority staff. This may go some of the way to explaining the divergence of opinion between ethnic minority and white nursing staff in their beliefs of which groups are most likely to be discriminated against in recruitment in the NHS.

Training and promotion

We asked staff members about their beliefs concerning racial discrimination in further training and promotional opportunities. Once again, respondents were asked whether they thought such racial discrimination was happening in the NHS in general, in their workplace in particular, and whether it had happened to them personally. The results to these questions are displayed in Table 13.3.

Table 13.3 Training and promotional opportunities within the NHS

	White	Black	Asian	Other	Not stated
Per cent believing training opportunities are refused *in the NHS* for ethnic reasons[1]	34	76	72	59	35
Per cent believing training opportunities are refused *in their workplace* for ethnic reasons[2]	14	57	54	43	17
Per cent believing training opportunities are refused *to them* for ethnic reasons[3]	0	23	25	12	1
Per cent believing *they* had been discriminated against in promotion for ethnic reasons[4]	0	23	28	17	1

[1] Total nursing staff (722 did not respond to this question)   13,608
[2] Total nursing staff (832 did not respond to this question   13,498
[3] Total nursing staff (422 did not respond to this question)   13,888
[4] Total nursing staff (525 did not respond to this question)   13,805

The first line of the table shows that large proportions of NHS staff believed that nursing staff in the NHS were sometimes denied the opportunity to go on training courses for reasons to do with their 'race' or colour. Even amongst the white staff, a third believed this to be the case, as did the majority of black, Asian and nursing staff from other ethnic minority groups.

This same pattern of results was found in response to the question concerning the existence of this form of racial discrimination in their own workplace, although, overall, staff were less likely to see discrimination here than in the NHS as a whole. The second line of Table 13.3 shows that over half of the black and Asian nursing staff believed that applicants in their workplace were denied opportunities to go on courses, compared with just under half of the nursing staff from other ethnic minority groups, and less than a fifth of white staff and those who did not state their ethnicity.

All respondents were asked whether they themselves had ever been denied the opportunity to go on a course for reasons to do with 'race' or colour, or if they had ever been denied a promotion for these reasons. The third and fourth lines of Table 13.3 show that the overwhelming majority of all staff members did not feel they had been discriminated against in this manner while working for the NHS. However, a significant proportion – approximately a quarter of the black and Asian staff – reported that they had had these experiences.

In summary, all groups of nursing staff were more likely to feel that discrimination existed within the NHS as a whole rather than in their own workplaces, regardless of personal experience. All groups thought that discrimination in recruitment was more likely than discrimination in training and promotional opportunities.

In answering these questions, interesting similarities and differences between the ethnic groups were revealed. A larger proportion of Asian staff members reported personal experience of racial discrimination than any other ethnic group. Asian nursing staff reported that this was most likely in opportunities for promotion. Black nursing staff were just as likely as Asian nursing staff to report racial discrimination in the area of recruitment. Similarly 'other' ethnic minority staff were also more likely to report racial discrimination in the area of recruitment and promotion.

Results for black nursing staff are similar to those found by Brown (1984). Although the professional and ethnic groups are not directly comparable the results are of some interest. A quarter of West Indian respondents in *Black & White Britain* (Brown 1984) reported that they had been refused a job on grounds they suspected were racial. Similarly, in our survey, over a quarter of black nursing staff reported recruitment discrimination. Interestingly, less than a tenth of Asian respondents in PSI's third national survey of ethnic minorities (Brown 1984) felt discriminated against in the area of recruitment and even less in the area of promotion. However, in our survey the situation is somewhat different with 26 per cent of Asian nursing staff reporting recruitment discrimination and 28 per cent suggesting they felt discriminated against in promotional opportunities. These findings are somewhat surprising given the results of the logistic regression (see Chapter 10) in which ethnicity was found to be a significant factor in predicting nursing grade, for black nurses only.

Who has training problems?

We went on to ask respondents who believed that opportunities to go on courses in the NHS or within their workplace were denied on the basis of 'race' or colour which groups, in their opinion, were most likely to be discriminated against. The results in Table 13.4 mirror the findings in the earlier recruitment section. More ethnic minority nursing staff thought that black or Asian nurses were more likely to be discriminated against than their white colleagues. In contrast we found that just over half of white nursing staff and nursing staff who did not declare their ethnicity felt that both white and black and Asian nurses were equally as likely to be discriminated against in this way.

Table 13.4 Who has training problems?

	White	Black	Asian	Other	Not stated
In the NHS in general[1]					
Per cent believing that *white* staff are discriminated against	1	0	2	0	2
Per cent believing that *black and Asian* staff are discriminated against	43	70	64	60	41
Per cent believing *white, black and Asian* staff are discriminated against	56	30	34	40	57
In my workplace[2]					
Per cent believing that *white* staff are discriminated against	3	1	1	0	4
Per cent believing that *black and Asian* staff are discriminated against	35	66	65	55	34
Per cent believing *white, black and Asian* staff are discriminated against	62	33	34	45	62

[1] Total nursing staff (269 did not respond to this question)   4,684

[2] Total nursing staff (107 did not respond to this question)   2,255

With respect to their own workplace, once again ethnic minority nursing staff were more likely to believe that black and Asian nurses were the main targets of discrimination in their workplaces. Again, this was in contrast to the answers given by white nursing staff and nursing staff who did not state their ethnicity.

If we compare these results with those found in the previous section on recruitment there are a number of interesting differences. In particular, respondents regardless of their ethnic group are more likely to feel that both white and black or Asian nurses are equally as likely to be racially discriminated against in opportunities to go on courses, than in recruitment opportunities within their workplaces. Some explanation of these results may be found in the case study chapters on recruitment, selection and training opportunities.

Equal opportunities

All respondents were asked if their employers had a policy of ensuring equal opportunities for people from all racial or ethnic groups. Findings were fairly similar across all ethnic groups, ranging from 68 per cent of black staff who knew that their employer had such a policy, to 75 per cent of staff from other ethnic minorities. It is of some interest that approximately a quarter of all nursing staff were unaware of whether or not their employer operated an equal opportunities policy. A small proportion of each group (ranging from 2 per cent to 5 per cent) said that their employer did not have such a policy. For more detailed information on nursing staff's perceptions of equal opportunities see Chapter 6.

In order to examine how much faith nursing staff had in the equal opportunities policies operated by their employer we asked them how effective they thought such a policy was. As Table 13.5 shows, most nursing staff felt their employer's equal opportunities policy was effective. However, there were wide variations between ethnic groups in opinions about the extent of this effectiveness. Almost all white nursing staff thought the policy was effective. But between one fifth and two fifths of the members of each minority group disagreed with the majority view.

There has been much debate about the re-grading exercise of clinical nursing staff in 1988 and its implication for equal opportunities (CRE 1992). Nursing staff were asked for their opinions on how fairly they felt the regrading exercise of 1988 had been carried out; and whether they felt that white and ethnic minority staff had been equally treated. Overall, no groups felt that ethnic minority nurses were given better treatment than their white colleagues in the 1988 regrading, as Table 13.6 shows. Beliefs

Table 13.5 Effectiveness of equal opportunities policy

Ethnic origin	Per cent believing in the effectiveness of employer equal opportunities policy	
	Effective	Not effective
White	96	4
Black	61	39
Asian	69	31
Other	79	21
Not stated	95	5
Total nursing staff	9,977	

varied by ethnic group with most white nursing staff believing that white and ethnic minority nursing staff were given equal treatment in the regrading exercise. But the minority groups themselves were fairly evenly divided as to whether the regrading had been fair in this sense, or not. It must be noted that a very large proportion of nursing staff regardless of their ethnic group were unsure and answered 'don't know' to this question.

Table 13.6 Bias in 1988 regrading

Ethnic origin	Per cent believing there was bias in the 1988 regrading			
	White and ethnic minorities given better treatment	Ethnic minorities given better treatment	Whites given better treatment	Don't know
White	54	2	3	41
Black	25	1	28	46
Asian	28	1	25	46
Other	38	1	14	47
Not stated	47	2	3	48
Total nursing staff	14,330			

To explore further the attitudes of staff members towards equal opportunities within the NHS we asked whether they felt that white and ethnic minority people had equal chances in nursing. None of the groups of nursing staff thought that ethnic minority people had better chances in nursing than white people. Just over half the black and Asian nursing staff believed that white people had better chances, while the remaining three groups felt the chances of different ethnicities were approximately equal. Again, the findings of this question must be interpreted with caution as a large group of respondents, regardless of ethnic group were unsure and answered that they did not know.

Table 13.7 Bias in NHS nursing

Ethnic origin	Per cent believing in a bias in NHS nursing for ethnic reasons			
	Whites and ethnic minorities have equal chance	Ethnic minorities have better chance	Whites have better chance	Don't know
White	58	2	14	25
Black	16	2	58	24
Asian	21	1	56	22
Other	32	1	41	26
Not stated	52	3	13	32
Total nursing staff	14,330			

Overall, we can see a pattern emerging. Groups that have little faith in the equal opportunities policies operated by their employers are also less likely to feel that the treatment of ethnic minorities was fair within the NHS. Those who felt that their employer's equal opportunities policies were generally effective were also more likely to feel that white and ethnic minority nursing staff were given equal treatment in the 1988 regrading exercise. But, regardless of this, all ethnic groups including whites are much less likely to feel that white and ethnic minority people have equal chances in nursing in the NHS.

Working relationships

All staff members were asked if they had experienced difficulties, hostilities or aggression from patients or from colleagues, for reasons to do with their 'race' or colour. The answers to these two questions are shown in Table 13.8, and in both cases responses were sharply divided on the basis of ethnic group. The majority of black and Asian nursing staff reported problems whereas, in contrast, only 12 per cent of white nursing staff and a tenth of nursing staff who had not stated their ethnic group reported similar difficulties.

Reports of hostilities from other nursing staff or management were less common, as the second line of the table demonstrates. However, approximately a third of nurses from ethnic minority groups reported that colleagues, supervisors or managers had behaved in a difficult, hostile or aggressive way towards them for reasons to do with 'race' or colour. In contrast only 3 per cent of white nursing staff and 4 per cent of nursing staff who did not state their ethnic group experienced similar difficulties.

Table 13.8 Racial harassment from patients and colleagues

	White	Black	Asian	Other	Not stated
Per cent indicating difficulties with patients for ethnic reasons[1]	12	66	58	48	10
Per cent indicating difficulties with colleagues for ethnic reasons[2]	3	37	37	32	4

[1] Total nursing staff (347 did not answer)	13,983	
[2] Total nursing staff (385 did not answer)	13,945	

Conclusion

This chapter has documented the level of knowledge amongst nursing staff and degree of faith held in equal opportunities policies. In addition detailed questions were asked on attitudes towards, and experience of discrimination and racial harassment while working in the NHS.

Overall there were wide variations between the beliefs and experiences of white and ethnic minority nursing staff. White nursing staff were much less likely to believe that racial discrimination occurred in recruitment, training and promotion, both within the NHS as a whole, and within their own particular workplaces. White nursing staff were also far less likely than their ethnic minority colleagues to have personal experience of such discrimination. In addition, where discrimination existed, white nursing staff were more likely to feel that both white and black or Asian nursing staff would be equally discriminated against, including in the 1988 regrading exercise. Unlike their ethnic minority colleagues nearly all white nursing staff held a high degree of faith in employers' equal opportunities policies and reported little experiences of 'difficulties' with patients or managers for reasons to do with 'race' or colour. In contrast, many nurses from ethnic minorities reported racial harassment from patients, and a significant proportion reported problems with colleagues.

PART IV

SUMMARY AND CONCLUSIONS

14 Summary of findings

This report presented results from a research project analysing aspects of the careers of NHS nursing and midwifery staff in a multi-ethnic society. The findings were presented in two parts; the first resulting from the qualitative case studies of six nurse employers, and the second from the national postal survey of nursing and midwifery staff.

Personnel policy and practice for NHS nurses and midwives in six case study areas
Results were presented from six qualitative case studies of NHS nurse and midwife employers, undertaken within six district authorities and trusts. A total of 156 interviews were conducted with nurses, midwives and managers from a range of levels and specialties. The case study results related to six main issues of personnel policy and practice as they affected NHS staff members. These areas were recruitment and selection procedures, the assessment of nursing staff, training and development, equal opportunities, flexible working arrangements and relationships with colleagues and patients.

Recruitment and selection

- Five of the case study nurse employers had written policies on recruitment; the sixth was in the process of formulating an overall policy following a major reorganisation.

- Most of the six case study employers used a combination of internal only or simultaneous internal and external advertisement. On the whole, the higher the grade of post, the more likely it was to be simultaneously advertised internally and externally.

- Three types of external advertisement were in use:
    - local press, job centres and other local media: these tended to be used for low-grade posts, especially auxiliaries, thought to be based on a local labour market;

- circulation of details of vacancies among nurses under threat of redundancy or displacement, through the London Implementation Group;

- national advertisements in the specialist press: these tended to be used for higher grade posts for qualified nurses.

The ethnic minority press tended to fall into the category of local general advertising, on the ground that there was no specialist medium for black or Asian nurses. Word of mouth was used as a way of finding suitable candidates but recruitment would never be restricted solely to informal channels.

- The ward manager and the senior nurse in the appropriate specialty normally took the lead in drafting an advertisement for a post, specifying a job and person description.

- Similarly, the appropriate ward manager and the senior nurse of the specialty would take responsibility for the shortlisting and interviewing of candidates. A representative from the personnel department would only become involved in the selection of senior nurse appointments, such as those for ward manager and above.

- In several of the nurse employers looked at, informal criteria in addition to, or sometimes instead of, a written specification were used. Interviewers did not always agree with, or follow, written criteria or structured scoring systems. In some cases, they treated the formal paperwork associated with the selection procedure as an unnecessary bureaucratic requirement and therefore did not record the actual reason why individuals were appointed or rejected.

- Only one of the six case study nurse employers had laid down guidelines for the training of those involved in the recruitment process.

The assessment of nursing staff

- In 1986, the then Department of Health and Social Security recommended that a formal system of appraisal in the form of the Individual Performance Review (IPR) should be extended to all staff working in the NHS.

- In theory, the IPR should consist of four stages:

  - the nurse and the manager should each consider the nurse's performance against a broad list of objectives;

- they should meet to discuss their views, and formulate a development programme to achieve specific objectives over the next year;

- the assessment and proposals for development should be agreed by the manager's own manager (the 'grandparent');

- the manager and nurse should meet at the end of the year to assess progress against the agreed objectives.

• Overall, the introduction of IPR in the six case study areas looked at was poor. It was found that only three of the six employers had introduced the IPR as a system of appraising their nursing staff. The remaining three case study areas operated informal appraisal systems undertaken at irregular intervals on undefined criteria.

• Even within the three case study areas where IPR had been introduced, implementation had been partial. In particular, there were three serious problems:

- First, the system of appraisal had not been introduced across all the nursing specialties within each employer.

- Secondly, it had yet to reach all nursing staff falling within the clinical nursing grading structure, with nursing staff below the grade of ward manager rarely being appraised.

- Thirdly, there were problems in actually carrying it out effectively with some nursing staff expressing concern about how an appraisal system which involved the appraiser and appraisee in such an open relationship would affect their day-to-day working relationships.

• The dissatisfaction regarding the slow progress towards implementing a formal system of appraisal like the IPR was as great amongst white staff as it was amongst ethnic minority staff. Without a formal system of assessment, decisions that are made with regard to promotion, limited as they are in the current climate, were seen as being subjective.

Training and development

• Although the process of application for training opportunities was similar across the six case study employers, the criteria upon which decisions were made to grant then were very varied.

- Four of the employers had no written criteria by which they granted training opportunities. As a result, the unwritten criteria upon which managers made such decisions ranged from the subjective, ad hoc and potentially unfair to the more systematic and formal.

- A further two employers had policy documents that stated that training opportunities for nursing staff would be identified through individual discussions with nursing staff as part of their regular performance appraisal. As we saw in the preceding section, the IPR system of appraisal was not in operation at all in three of the employers, whilst in the remainder it was not operating effectively in relation to staff below the grade of ward manager. Hence, in many cases, the allocation of training opportunities was not taking place as it was supposed to.

- Overall, however, it seemed that the lack of training opportunities was a problem facing all staff, irrespective of ethnicity. Most nurses and midwives perceived unwritten and informal criteria as being an unfair and potentially discriminatory way by which to allocate training and development opportunities.

- A related issue of central concern to most nursing staff, but particularly those below the level of ward manager, was the feeling that they were effectively being prevented from taking up training opportunities because of the constraints imposed on them by an ever decreasing training budget and staff shortages. Consequently, employers were increasingly expecting nursing staff to pay for courses themselves and do them in their own time.

Equal opportunities

- All of the six case study employers had adopted formal equal opportunities policies. Most covered broadly the same ground, but in slightly different ways:

  - a list of the types of people at risk of discrimination, and an affirmation of action to prevent unfair treatment;

  - reference to legislation (such as the Race Relations Act) and to the roles of statutory bodies (such as the Commission for Racial Equality);

  - details of personnel procedures designed to be fair. Some policies had sections dealing in detail with the three main areas of potential discrimination: race, gender and disability;

- methods of communicating the policy to staff, potential recruits and others;

- responsibility for the implementation of the policy identified as resting with general management, line management and staff. Each of these should ensure that they themselves and the next in line were aware of the policy, had received training and adhered to it. Only one employer, however, had appointed a working group with specific responsibility for overseeing the effective implementation of the equal opportunities policy;

- collection of information about candidates to enable the policy to be monitored; but few of the policies explained how the data were to be analysed;

- staff wishing to complain of discrimination or harassment to be advised to take the matter up informally at first, then formally if not resolved;

- some policies to spread the aims wider: to contracting organisations; to the treatment of patients.

• Although all the policies stated how selection and other procedures ought to work, many of them were unclear about how the policy would be enforced, and how its effectiveness could be evaluated. This lack of clarity over enforcement was clearly reflected in the fact that action plans were not in operation, except in one area.

• Within most of the six case study employers, equal opportunities strategies broke down in one or more of three areas. These were:

- the communication of the policy and its application on a day to day basis;

- the analyses of any monitoring information;

- the development of action plans.

• If it existed, training was variable. The combination of these factors meant that, overall, employers could be characterised as having intentions rather than actions. These intentions were sometimes very ambitious, but if the practice was insufficient, the intentions were of no use.

• Most nursing and midwifery staff were aware of the existence of their employers equal opportunities policy. However, their perceptions of such polices largely reflected the lack of clear practice. There was a tendency for staff to be quite cynical about the effectiveness of such policies and they were very much perceived as being paper promises.

• In the light of our findings, it is not surprising that much of the nursing workforce was unconvinced of their employer's commitment to equal opportunities. It was widely felt that ethnic minorities were underrepresented in senior positions within nursing management. For some ethnic minority staff this was a confirmation that opportunities were not equally distributed at all.

Flexible working arrangements and child care

• In the postal survey, women were found to make up over 90 per cent of the NHS nursing staff. Many of the staff, both men and women, had children under sixteen. This means that flexible working arrangements and child care provision are of primary importance within the NHS, both in terms of enhancing staff development and in terms of retaining staff and providing a stable service.

• The NHS Management Executive and the Department of Health are committed to addressing the issues of equal opportunities for women in the NHS and a large part of this is to ensure the equal availability of flexible working arrangements. Flexible working arrangements can include types of special leave, job sharing, career breaks, flexitime and term-time only working.

• The interviews carried out in the six case study areas confirmed the findings in the quantitative postal survey relating to the high levels of part-time working amongst the nursing staff. However, the interviews suggested that part-time workers and those working nights only felt that their access to career development options such as further training were restricted by their hours. Beyond part-time working, few staff reported use of job-share arrangements – again, confirming the postal survey which found that only one per cent of staff were in job-shares. The interviews suggested that the large numbers of staff with young children felt unable to lose half their salary as the income was especially necessary with young families.

• All six case study areas offered staff child care facilities, which were usually workplace creches or nurseries. However, they were usually tied to normal working hours and were not always appropriate for staff working shifts or weekends.

- Despite written policies, there were a number of ways in which flexible working and child care provisions by the employers did not reflect the needs of the nursing staff.

Relations with colleagues and patients

- The racial harassment of ethnic minority nurses continues to be a regular feature of their working lives in the NHS. In every case study looked at and in nearly every specialty within these areas, ethnic minority nurses reported being racially harassed by patients.

- Broadly speaking, this racial harassment from patients could be broken down into two distinct forms. First, there was a form of harassment where the racial motivation in the incidents was clear because of the accompanying verbal insults or because the patient had made it clear they did not want to be 'nursed' by an ethnic minority nurse. Secondly, there was a more subtle form of racial harassment where white patients did not explicitly mention the nurse's ethnicity, but rather treated ethnic minority nurses in a relatively unfavourable way to their manners with white nurses.

- Some ethnic minority nurses also reported being subjected to racial harassment from fellow colleagues. Although the study found that the extent of racial harassment suffered by ethnic minority nursing staff from colleagues was not as great as that from patients, it remains an issue of concern, particularly in those cases where the perpetrator was identified as being a nurse manager, with control over the allocation of training opportunities and further career development.

- The study found that the large majority of incidents of racial harassment were not reported to senior management. This was because there was a perception amongst ethnic minority victims that their complaint would not be supported by management. Indeed, it seemed to be the case that ethnic minority nursing and midwifery staff were simply expected to ignore such harassment because it was considered unprofessional to be upset or get hurt by comments made by patients. As a result, racially abusive behaviour had come to be the norm in the nursing workplace and in some case study areas had become an inextricable aspect of the culture of the workplace.

- On those few occasions when senior management sought to tackle the problem, ethnic minority staff thought their response was inadequate. Written polices to address the problem of racial harassment were not sufficiently comprehensive because they only covered incidents involving colleagues and not patients. We saw in the relevant chapter that racial harassment from patients was by far the greater problem facing ethnic minority staff.

Results of the postal survey

To provide a more informed basis for the discussion of racial discrimination against ethnic minority nursing staff in the NHS, a major postal survey was conducted, collecting detailed information from 14,330 nursing staff, all of whom were in permanent jobs at the time of the survey, and who between them represented the breadth of the nursing grading structure from A to I. The questionnaire contained details about the current post; reports of relations with colleagues and patients; information from nursing staff about opportunities for training and career development, equal opportunities and experience of racial discrimination and harassment. The nursing staff members who took part were selected from certain areas in the country to ensure adequate numbers of respondents from ethnic minority groups, and the sample was then weighted to correct for this sampling bias.

The first two chapters of results from the postal survey concentrated on a profile of employment characteristics and career paths of both white and ethnic minority respondents in order to compare them. The last three chapters of results from the postal survey presented information on the beliefs and attitudes of white and ethnic minority nursing staff on the extent of racial or ethnic discrimination. The main results are outlined below.

Employment characteristics and career paths of NHS nursing and midwifery staff

The results from the first part of the postal survey shed light on the backgrounds and characteristics of NHS nursing staff at the current time, and looked at the factors that might be related to grade level, including ethnicity.

- Approximately eight per cent of the staff were from ethnic minority groups, mainly black and Asian.

- Only seven per cent of the nursing staff in the survey were male, and the Asian nursing staff were more likely to be male than the other ethnic groups.

- On average, the nursing staff were 40 years old and nearly half had children under 16.

- The majority of nursing staff were registered nurses, with or without post-registration qualifications. The majority were to be found in the core professional grades, C, D and E.

- Differences between the ethnic minority nursing staff and their white peers were obvious from the start. Ethnic minority nursing staff were older than white nursing staff, had fewer general educational qualifications, and were more likely to be working in specialties such as mental illness and learning disabilities, rather than in the more prestigious medical and community based specialties.

- Ethnic minority nursing staff tended to have been in the profession longer than their white peers, and had been in their current posts longer. They were also more likely to be working full-time, and to be doing other paid work on top of their jobs.

- However, a straightforward comparison of grade level did not suggest clear differences between the ethnic groups. Asian nursing staff were less likely than other groups (including white nursing staff) to be unqualified. The ethnic minority groups were relatively well represented in the higher grades.

- A general model of predicting nursing level (as measured by grade level) was developed, including the background characteristics that people bring to the job, the various features of their nursing career such as getting extra qualifications, and aspects of their work such as the area of specialty in which they work. At all levels, staff qualifications, length of time in the nursing profession, and specialty worked in, were significant predictors of grade attainment. In addition, the chance of having a higher grade was generally greater for male staff, and for those with higher levels of general education.

- Finally, the role of ethnicity in predicting nursing grade was assessed by adding it to the model as a final step. There were no indications of minorities being at a disadvantage in access to middle-ranking posts, up to grade E. Indeed, Asians were *more* likely than their white counterparts to have reached grade E. But blacks were at a significant disadvantage in access to grades F and above. There were some indications that Asians may also have been slightly slower to reach these senior grades.

Perceptions, attitudes and work experiences of nursing and midwifery staff in the NHS

The second part of the postal survey results took the perspective of the nursing staff and looked at the ways in which they construe their training opportunities and various aspects of their jobs generally.

- Information about courses was available to staff, and many managed to register for further training.

- However, difficulties arose in getting employers to provide paid time-off, and to provide course fee payments.

- Against this general background of restricted resources, ethnic minority nursing staff reported very similar levels of ease and difficulty with respect to the different aspects of acquiring further training.

- Generally, ethnic minority nursing staff reported more racial discrimination in their workplaces with respect to a range of issues than white staff. They reported racial discrimination in recruitment and training opportunities.

- However, they reported most discrimination when asked generally about the NHS, less when asked about their own workplace, and least when asked if they themselves had experienced any. Approximately a quarter believed that they had been denied opportunities because of their ethnicity.

- The postal survey showed that almost all nurses agreed that members of ethnic minorities experience racial discrimination or racial harassment in the NHS. The case studies show that these problems take many different forms.

- About a quarter of minority nurses in the postal survey thought that they themselves had been discriminated against in recruitment, training or promotion. The evidence from the postal survey suggests that many of them may have been right, at least among the black nurses, although it is difficult to pin this down in individual cases.

- About a third of members of minority groups in the postal survey said they had experienced racial difficulties in relationships with other nurses. Many of those interviewed in depth told about occasions when they had been ignored, talked about and been racially abused.

- Up to two-thirds of the black, Asian and 'other' minority nurses in the postal survey said that they had been racially harassed by patients.

The case histories confirmed that this is much the most widespread problem; nurses reported incident after incident of racial abuse from the very people they were trying to help. Some victims explained patients' racism in terms of their age or mental condition; others felt they just had to put up with it.

- Although senior management had declared its opposition to racial harassment, and had set up informal and formal procedures for dealing with it, few of the people who felt that they had experienced these problems had taken them up with the authorities. It was widely believed that nothing could be done about racist attitudes among patients, though occasionally a sister would intervene on a nurse's behalf. The initiative for dealing with harassment within the workforce lay with the victims, rather than with line managers. Members of the minority groups were reluctant to call on formal procedures which might alienate them further from their colleagues. There were few examples of successful disciplinary action.

15 Conclusions and policy implications

The relationship between policy and practice

If there is an overall conclusion, it is not a very surprising one: that there is a big gap between the theoretical policies identified by senior and general managers and the actual practices undertaken on the ward and in other workplaces, as evidenced in the responses of the nurses to the qualitative and quantitative surveys.

Senior staff responsible for managing the human resources of the whole health authority or trust all agreed on how things might ideally be done. They agreed that:

- procedures for recruitment and promotion should be clearly laid down, and that the people involved should be trained in their use;

- the development of each member of staff should be assessed annually. They agreed that training opportunities should be determined by consideration of the needs of the service and the development needs of the individual;

- special attention needed to be paid to equal opportunities for groups who have been discriminated against in the past;

- staff needed some flexibility in work patterns, and opportunities for career breaks, especially those associated with raising a family a matter of particular importance for a profession with so large a proportion of women.

While senior management accepted all these objectives, there is a series of steps between the intention and the achievement:

- formulating a full policy;

- communicating the policy to those expected to act upon it;

- training them in the detailed implications;

- ensuring that they adhere to the procedures;

- monitoring the outcome, to find out if the desired objective has been achieved.

One of the main themes of this report has been that these steps have not been followed through. Although there were many policies, very few employers knew if they had been successful. All the employers had full equal opportunities policies, and five out of six had general statements on recruitment procedures. Only three employers had even partially introduced full appraisal schemes. Few had clearly worked out policies about the allocation of training opportunities or career breaks.

But even where there was a policy, the people who had to implement them – the middle and line managers such as ward sisters – were often unclear about what the policy was, and how they were supposed to undertake their responsibilities within it. Only some of them had been trained in these activities. Many were having to work it out for themselves, and hardly anyone felt that their own managers, or the personnel department, would 'catch them' if they did not adhere to the procedures. Clearly, some employers, and some groups within employers, were in advance of others in all these respects. But no employer could claim that all their policies were fully implemented.

Finally, we found little if any evidence that those responsible for formulating a policy were analysing the outcomes in ways which would help them to decide whether it was being carried out, or whether it was having the desired effect. Quite a lot of monitoring information was *collected* (information was recorded on forms and sent to the personnel department); only some of it was ever *processed* (in the sense that tables were produced); hardly any of it was *analysed and assessed* (in the sense of helping to take decisions about future action).

These conclusions imply that more emphasis should be given to managing the implementation of existing policies, and making effective use of existing ethnic monitoring information.

Nurses' reports of racial discrimination and harassment

The fact that nurse employers, like many other types of employer, depart from ideal personnel procedures does not mean managers take unfair decisions affecting nurses' careers. However, it does allow unfair considerations to enter the decision-making process, so that the general management cannot be sure that equal opportunities are being provided. An important finding to emerge was that both white and ethnic minority nursing staff reported a general sense of unfairness. In addition, however, ethnic minority nursing staff also quite often suspected racial discrimination by their managers and they were more likely to feel the system was not as fair as it should be and allowed discrimination. On the other hand, for white nursing staff, ethnicity was not always the primary issue. Finally, there was one feature of life in a hospital or community nursing service which was specific to ethnic minority nurses and midwives – racial harassment. Both the qualitative interviews and the quantitative survey identified racism within working relationships, which is unacceptable. Similarly, racial harassment from patients was widespread, and often blatant. As with so many other aspects of personnel policy, management was not seen to be doing anything about either of these problems.

The implications of these findings are clear. The role of management in dealing with the racial harassment experiences of nurses is crucial. The paths for reporting such incidents should be developed, and staff need to feel more confident that they will receive support. Outlines for basic good practice with respect to dealing with harassment reports exist already; again it is implementation that is the central issue.

The role of ethnicity in nursing and midwives grading placements
The qualitative interviews provided background information on policies and practices, suggesting that both were influenced by many different factors, set against the background of the changing NHS. The results from the postal survey were very important in highlighting some of the complexities inherent in the experiences of nursing staff in a multi-cultural society. It is not enough simply to compare the grading structure of nursing staff from different ethnicities and draw conclusions based solely on such cross-sectional analyses. It is only when all the factors are considered, including personal characteristics, career details and features of the working environment, that some of the more important results begin to emerge.

The statistical analyses presented in this report made the first step in this direction, suggesting that certain ethnic minorities seem to be at a particular disadvantage within the nursing profession, particularly black nurses. On the other hand, the magnitude of the differences between the ethnic minority groups and the white group were never huge, and many of the problems encountered by ethnic minority nursing staff were also encountered by white nursing staff, including difficulties in finding financial support for further training. It should be noted that even where ethnicity did appear to have a statistically independent effect (for predicting which nurses would be in the higher nursing grades of F and G) its effect was not as powerful as that found for various educational and qualification factors that nurses brought to their jobs. In addition, at one point in the grading scale, Asian nursing and midwifery staff seemed to have a higher chance of having reached a grade (grade E) than white staff. However, despite the complexities in the pattern, the fact that ethnicity still had a part to play, even after controlling for these other factors, is an important finding and one that warrants further investigation. It is particularly important to establish the cause for this difference, be it direct discrimination by health service managers, or some other aspect of cultural difference between ethnic groups.

Both parts of the research project showed that members of ethnic minority groups feel that discrimination is still a major problem in the NHS, and in this respect their perceptions differ from their white colleagues. These perceptions are an important part of their attitude to their work and will, no doubt, affect the ability of the NHS to retain them in the future. Whatever the magnitude of the difficulties, both the reality of ethnic minority differences in nurse career patterns, and the perceptions of discrimination, remain problems for the NHS, and should remain the topic of further intensive study.

Implications for policy
The research findings indicate two main ways in which nursing staff from ethnic minority groups were disadvantaged within the National Health Service: some of them have fallen behind in the competition for senior nursing posts; most face racial harassment from patients and many of them from colleagues. What should employers do about these problems?

The NHS Management Executive has already established a programme of action for ethnic minority staff (NHSME 1993). It includes three general goals relevant to all types of staff:

- *Recruitment and selection:* NHS trusts and health authorities to include in their business plans, within a specific timescale, a local objective to increase the proportion of ethnic minority staff in areas and grades where they are underrepresented until fair representation is achieved;

- *Staff development:* To maximise the skills and potential of all personnel in a multi-racial NHS workforce, with particular emphasis on the identifiable needs of people from ethnic minority groups;

- *Racial harassment:* To ensure that NHS workplaces are free from harassment and discrimination, including racial harassment.

And among five specific goals, one referred to nursing staff:

- *Nurses:* NHS authorities and trusts to set a local objective to achieve equitable representation of ethnic minority nurses at G grade (ward manager or community equivalent) within five years. Progress towards achieving this objective should be reviewed annually as part of the business planning cycle.

Our case studies were undertaken just before this programme was published, and the postal survey just afterwards. The research was therefore contemporary with the policy initiative, and cannot show what effect it might have. The findings and implications of this study should therefore be seen as adding emphasis and detail to the existing policy, as it affects nursing staff, rather than as a substitute or critique.

No-one suggests that managers want the disadvantages faced by nurses from ethnic minority groups to persist. Those interviewed in the case studies were keen that they should be eliminated. The challenge is to allocate clear responsibility for making sure that they are tackled effectively.

The initial responsibility for these issues rests with corporate management. It is they who have to take the initiative for making their policies work more effectively. The case histories suggest that the responsibility is all too easily passed from group to group. Corporate management sets up a policy, but finds that line managers do not implement it properly. Line managers report that corporate management has not explained and enforced its policies. Staff end up feeling that the policy exists on paper only, and that no one really cares enough to make sure that it actually works.

While the responsibility for employers' policies clearly lies with the employing organisations themselves, other organisations could play a supportive role. The *Department of Health* and the *NHS Management Executive* have already developed guidelines and encouraged exchange of ideas and information. The *staff side organisations* have a strong interest in promoting active equal opportunities policies, at both national and local levels. And *purchaser organisations* are entitled to know what providers are doing about the ethnic composition of their workforce, especially if the minorities form a substantial proportion of the patients in the catchment area.

There are two important areas for consideration: improvements to human resource management policies to ensure that all nurses receive training and promotion opportunities appropriate to their skills and ambitions; and tackling racial harassment. Both of these issues need to be addressed in the context of local structures and working relationships.

Equal opportunities policies

Every NHS employer could consider two responses to the research findings: a broad-ranging review of the implementation of equal opportunities policies; and an immediate analysis of the career progress of black nurses.

As we have suggested, although most employers have an equal opportunities policy, these policies typically fall down somewhere between intention and outcome. No organisation can claim to have a successful policy until they can show that they are making progress towards the desired objective. The whole of the process illustrated in Figure 15.1 needs to be considered.

Clearly, the *implementation* of a policy is as important as the policy itself.

1. Most employers have *developed a policy*, and most nurses and midwives in the study were happy with the contents of those policies in principle. That is not the issue.

2. Once the policy has been developed and agreed, it needs to be *communicated*: everyone concerned, managers and staff, need to know what the policy is, what procedures have been developed, and what the objectives are. A popular summary could be distributed, posters placed on noticeboards and so on, with guidance on where to obtain more information, and what individuals should do if they do not think the policy is working.

3. The people directly responsible for the implementation of the policy need to be *trained* in the procedures that have been decided upon. Much of the responsibility for recruitment, assessment, training and promotion falls in practice on the shoulders of line managers senior and middle level nurses. But personnel work is not their primary activity, and each employer needs to decide:

   - how much training individual line managers require to participate in the agreed procedures;

   - to what extent personnel specialists should be provided to support managers in these activities;

   - how staff-side representatives should be involved in the process.

4. The people responsible for operating the procedure should not feel that it is up to them to decide whether to adhere to it. However good their intentions, busy people will soon learn to cut corners unless there is some process of *enforcement*. This does not require heavy-handed disciplinary action: a checklist of the procedures required on each

Figure 15.1 Implementation and assessment of an equal opportunities policy

Implementation	Assessment

1. Development of policy ⟵——————— 8. Reconsideration

2. Communication   7. Assessment of effect

3. Training in procedures   6. Analysis of outcomes

4. Enforcement of procedures ——————⟶ 5. Monitoring information

---

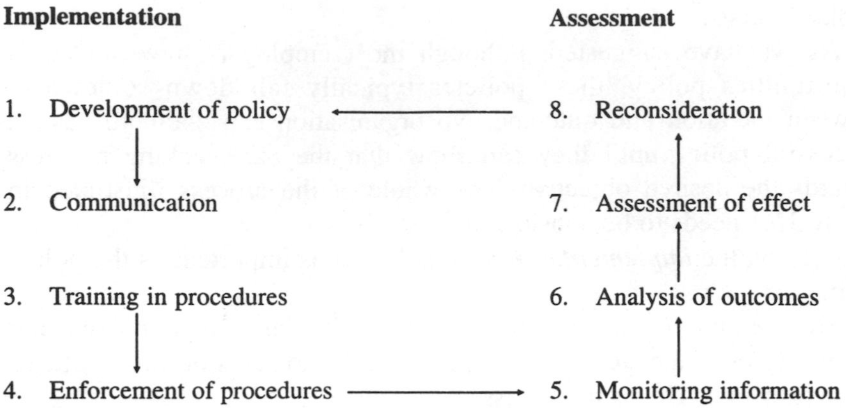

occasion, together with the active involvement of personnel specialist and staff representatives, should be adequate in most cases.

Implementation is clearly the most important, and the most time-consuming, part of the process. But few policies will work as intended without regular checks and revisions, so a procedure for the *assessment* of an equal opportunities policy is also essential.

5. *Information* needs to be collected about the implementation and outcome of the procedures. The information required should be thought out carefully in terms of the analysis that will be undertaken, identifying key indicators of performance rather than collecting data for their own sake.

6. The data then need to be processed and *analysed*. Again, the analysis requirements should be based on the need to understand the processes at work, rather than the mere production of tables. It is at this stage that current monitoring procedures fail. The case studies suggested that the representation and prospects of members of ethnic minority groups vary between different specialties within the same employer; the monitoring system should therefore be designed to measure progress in each department separately.

7. The key to the *assessment* stage is that someone should examine and interpret the data, to decide how the policy is working, and where the problems occur.

8. The policy should then be *reconsidered*, and revised, in the light of the findings of the monitoring programme.

Whereas the implementation of an equal opportunities policy can be undertaken only by the employing organisation itself, it might be appropriate for employers to club together at regional level, or even nationally, to develop the assessment stage. There would be two advantages:

- The design of data collection and analysis procedures, and interpretation of the results, are specialist research tasks. It would be much more efficient for a central team of experts to develop a system, than for each employer to try to invent the same wheel;

- Common data collection and analysis systems would allow comparison of how different types of equal opportunities policy were more or less successful at achieving their objectives. Employers who pooled their experience could develop models of good practice which could be more effective than each of the policies developed in isolation.

Better implementation and assessment of recruitment, training and promotion policies, discussed in the preceding paragraph, represent a wide-ranging and long-term response to the research findings. A precise and immediate response would also be appropriate. Every employer could reassess the career progress of every nurse in the middle and senior grades, paying particular attention to black staff near the boundary between grades E and F. We now know that many of them have fallen behind their white colleagues, with similar levels of training and experience, in entry to the senior grades. A scheme of personal development plans could be designed to increase the rate of promotion over the next few years, until a more equitable balance had been achieved. This would not mean that black nurses should be preferred to white ones in promotion competitions; it would mean that all groups were offered equivalent opportunities.

Racial harassment

Most nurse employers have a three-part policy on harassment. The equal opportunities policy contains a declaration that harassment is not approved of; individual nurses who experience harassment are encouraged to respond to the problem informally if they can; a grievance procedure is available if necessary. But the policy did not seem to be effective:

members of ethnic minority groups were still being harassed, and did not feel there was anything they could do about it.

As with the equal opportunities policy, the issue is one of responsibility. Existing policies leave much of the responsibility for dealing with racial harassment to the victims. They are expected to respond informally at first; and to file a complaint against the offender if that does not work. Clearly such avenues of complaint after the event should be retained, but racial harassment would be dealt with much more effectively if every nurse (and every manager, doctor, technician and support staff member) was personally committed to an ethos in which overt racial prejudice was unacceptable. If that was the case, few people would be inclined to racially harass their colleagues; and many people would be available to support the victim and reprimand the offender whenever it did happen.

It is not suggested that the problem should be *left* to the responsibility of every individual; it would be managers' job to *make* it everyone's responsibility. This issue will not respond to heavy-handed tactics of management edict backed up by threats of disciplinary action. What is required is a carefully thought out campaign to convince staff that racial harassment is an unacceptable feature of NHS life, and that everyone's help is needed to prevent it. The issue needs to be discussed openly, perhaps at regular staff meetings or in specially convened groups. The professional associations and trade unions have an important role to play, not only in supporting their black and Asian members, but also in persuading their white members to think about the problem. This is not a problem which can be solved by outsiders. It requires a collective decision inside every hospital.

Summary of recommendations

We therefore propose that every NHS employer should take three actions in response to this research.

* First, to make sure that their equal opportunities policy is actually implemented and to produce information to show how effective it has been.

* Second, to undertake a case-by-case review of the development and promotion prospects of individual nurses, especially black staff near the boundary between grades E and F.

* Third, to initiate a campaign to make every employee feel responsible for supporting ethnic minority groups and preventing racial harassment.

Bibliography

Advisory Conciliation and Arbitration Service (1988) *Employee appraisal* (London: ACAS)

Akinsanya, J. (1988) 'Ethnic minority nurses, midwives and health visitors: what role for them in the National Health Service?' in *New Community* Vol.14 pp.444-450

Alexander, Z. and Dewjee, A. (eds) (1984) *Wonderful adventures of Mrs. Seacole in many lands* (Bristol: Falling Wall Press)

Alimo-Metcalfe, B. (1993) 'A woman's ceiling: a man's floor' in *Health Service Journal* Vol.103 No. 5374, 14 October pp.25-27

Althauser, R.P. and Kalleberg, A.L. (1981) 'Firms, occupations, and the structure of labour markets: a conceptual analysis' in I. Berg (ed.) *Sociological perspectives on labour markets* (New York: Academic Press) pp.119-45.

Aye Maung, N. and Mirrlees-Black, C. (1994) *Racially motivated crime: a British Crime Survey analysis* (London: Home Office)

Baxter, C. (1988) *The Black nurse: an endangered species* (Cambridge: Training in Health and Race)

Bevan, S. and Thompson, M. (1992) *An overview of policy and practice, Performance Management: an analysis of the issues* (London: Institute of Personnel Management)

Brading, E. and Wright, V. (1990) *Performance-related pay*, Personnel Management Factsheets, No. 30 (London: Personnel Publications)

Brown, C. (1984) *Black and White Britain: The Third PSI Survey* (London: Heinemann Educational Books)

Commission for Racial Equality (1983) *Ethnic minority hospital staff* (London: CRE)

Commission for Racial Equality (1989) 'Training: the implementation of equal opportunities at work' in *Policy and Planning* Vol.1 (London: CRE)

Commission for Racial Equality (1991) *A measure of equality: monitoring and achieving racial equality in employment* (London: CRE)

Commission for Racial Equality (1992) *Clinical nurse grading: the costs of a 'colour-blind' approach* (London: CRE)

Commission for Racial Equality (1994) *Race Relations Code of Practice for the elimination of racial discrimination and the promotion of equality of opportunity in employment* (London: CRE)

Department of Health (1989) *The Health Service: Caring for the 1990s* Working for Patients White Paper (London: Department of Health)

Department of Health (1991) *NHS workforce in England* (London: Department of Health)

Department of Health (1994) *NHS workforce in England* (London: Department of Health)

Ellis, B. (1990) *Racial equality: the nursing profession* (London: Kings Fund Equal Opportunities Task Force)

Finlayson, L.R., Ford, R. and Marsh, A. (1995) 'The rising cost of child care' in *Employment Gazette* December

Fletcher, C. and Williams, R. (1992) *Performance management: an analysis of the issues* (London: Institute of Personnel Management)

Gatley, E. (1993) 'PREP: from novice to expert' in *British Journal of Nursing* Vol.1 No.2 pp.88-91

Goss, S. and Brown, H. (1991) *Equal Opportunities for women in the NHS* (London: NHS Management Executive, Department of Health)

Haskey, J. (1991) 'Ethnic minority populations resident in private households estimates by county and metropolitan district of England and Wales' in *Population Trends* No.63 Spring pp. 22-35

Home Office (1977) *Racial discrimination: a guide to the Race Relations Act 1976* (London: HMSO)

Iganski, P. (1992) 'Reviving the concept of "Institutional Racism": effective policy implementation against racial discrimination at work'. Paper presented to the annual meeting of the American Sociological Association, Pittsburgh, 20-24 August

Institute of Health Services Management (1991) *Individual Performance Review in the NHS* (London: Institute of Health Services Management)

Jackson, C. and Barber, L. (1993) *Women in the NHS: experiences in South east Thames* (Brighton: Institute of Manpower Studies)

Jenkins, R. (1986) *Racism and recruitment: managers, organisations and equal opportunity in the labour market* (Cambridge: Economic and Social Research Council)

Jewson, N. and Mason, D. (1984) 'Equal opportunities policies at the workplace and the concept of monitoring' in *New Community* Vol.12 No.1 Winter 1984/85 pp.124-136

Jewson, N., Mason, D., Lambkin, C. and Taylor, F. (1992) *Ethnic monitoring policy and practice: a study of employer's experiences* (Leicester: Ethnic Minority Employment Research Centre, University of Leicester)

Jones, J.E. and Woodcock, M. (1987) *Manual of management development programme improvement* (Aldershot: Gower)

Jones, T. (1993) *Britain's ethnic minorities* (London: Policy Studies Institute)

Kline, R. (1993) 'Measuring down: PRP pitfalls' in *Health Visitor* Vol.66 No.6 June pp.13-15

Labour Research Department (1992) *Working parents: negotiating a better deal* (London: Labour Research Department)

Laing, W. (1994) *Managing the NHS: past, present and agenda for the future* (London: Office of Health Economics)

Long, P. (1986) *Performance appraisal revisited* (London: Institute of Personnel Management)

Mangan, P. (1993a) 'Preparation of change' in *Nursing Times* Vol.89 No.17 April pp.58-60

Mangan, P. (1993b) 'Paying the piper' in *Nursing Times* Vol.89 No.18 May pp.42-43

Marsh, A. and McKay, S. (1993) 'Families, work and the use of child care' in *Employment Gazette* August pp.361-370

Mayhew, P., Elliot, D. and Dowds, L. (1989) *The 1988 British Crime Survey* (London: HMSO)

McRae, S. (1991) *Maternity rights in Britain: the PSI report on the experience of women and employers* (London: Policy Studies Institute)

Morton-Williams, J. and Berthoud, R. (1971a) *Nurses attitude study: report on depth interviews* (London: Social Community Planning Research)

Morton-Williams, J. and Berthoud, R. (1971b) *Nurses attitude study: report on postal survey* (London: Social Community Planning Research)

Morton-Williams, J. and Berthoud, R. (1971c) *Nurses attitude study: report on personal interview survey* (London: Social Community Planning Research)

NHS Management Executive (1993) *Ethnic minority staff in the NHS: a programme of action* (London: National Health Service Management Executive, Department of Health)

NHS Training Directorate (1986) *Guide and model documentation for Individual Performance Review* (Bristol: National Health Service Training Directorate, Department of Health)

NHS Training Directorate (1992) *Realising potential a practical guide to equality of opportunity in management development* (Bristol: National Health Service Training Directorate, Department of Health)

National Union of Public Employees (NUPE) (1992) *Women in the NHS: a time for positive action* (London: NUPE)

Price Waterhouse (1988) *Nurse recruitment and retention: a report on the factors affecting the retention and recruitment of nurses, midwives and health visitors in the NHS* (London: Price Waterhouse)

Review Body for Nursing Staff, Midwives, Health Visitors and Professions Allied to Medicine (1994) *Eleventh report on nursing, midwives and health visitors 1994* (London: HMSO)

Rowe, H. (1992) 'How am I doing and where am I going? Individual performance review in staff appraisal' in *Professional Nurse* February pp.288-291

Smith, D.J. (1980) *Overseas doctors in the National Health Service* (London: Policy studies Institute)

Smith, M. and Robertson, I.T. (1993) *The theory and practice of systematic personnel selection* (London: Macmillan)

Storey, J. (1992) *Developments in the management of human resources* (Oxford: Blackwell Publishers)

Storey, J. and Sisson, K. (1993) *Managing human resources and industrial relations* (Buckingham: Open University Press)

Thomas, M. and Morton-Williams, J. (1972) *Overseas nurses in Britain* (London: Political Economic Planning)

Townley, B. (1991) 'Selection and appraisal: reconstituting 'social relations'?' in J.Storey (ed.) *New Perspectives on human resource management* (London: Routledge)

UKCC (1986) *Project 2000: a new preparation for practice* (London: UKCC)

UKCC (1991) *Statistical analysis of the council's professional register*, 1 April 1990 to 31 March 1991 (London: UKCC)

Virdee, S. (1995) *Racial violence and harassment* (London: Policy Studies Institute)

APPENDICES

Appendix 1

The management topic guide used in case study areas

Recruitment
1. Can you tell me how you would recruit a staff nurse (midwife)?

Advertisements
Where do you advertise?

Probe:
Contents of advert
Other ways of letting people know

Job description
Do you have a written job description?

Probe:
Contents
Who has input into development?
Shortlisting:
Do you shortlist candidates?

Probe:
Who shortlists?
What factors determine selection?
Are people who shortlist trained?

Interviewing
How do you evaluate people at the interview stage?

Probe:
Who sits on the interview panel?
What factors determine appointment?

Do staff who sit on panel have to undertake training?

2. Is the recruitment process the same for:
    a. an unqualified nurse
    b. a senior nurse (e.g. a ward manager/ sister)
    If not, how is it different?

Training
3. Can you tell me your role in the area of training opportunities?

Probe:
If not involved, who is?

4. Do staff nurses (midwives) have any opportunities for further training?

Probe:
What opportunities do they have?
How can they get to know about the opportunities?
Is anything done to encourage ethnic minority staff to participate in training?

5. Who generally takes the initiative on training? Is the staff nurse expected to find out what is available and apply, or does a manager nominate people to go on courses, or suggest to them they apply?

Probe:
Who decides whether a staff nurse (midwife) may go on a training course?
What factors are taken into account?
Who pays for the training?

6. Are there similar opportunities for training for:
    a. an unqualified nurse
    b. a senior nurse (e.g. a ward manager/ sister)
    If not, what opportunities for training do they have?

Staff appraisals
7. How is a staff nurse (midwife) assessed?

Probe:
Who evaluates a nurse's performance? (Are these staff trained?)
What factors are taken into account?
How often are nurses assessed?

8. Is there a written record of a staff nurse's (midwife's) appraisal?

Probe:
How can nurses ask to look at it?
Can they discuss it with someone?
Are they able to appeal against their appraisal?
How can they get to find out about this procedure?

9. Is the assessment procedure the same for:
   a. an unqualified nurse
   b. a senior nurse (e.g a ward manager/ sister)
   If not, how is it different?

Promotion
10. Can you tell me how you would promote a staff nurse (midwife)?

Probe:
Adverts
Job description
Shortlisting
Interviewing
Training for those who shortlist and appoint

11. Would the process of promotion be the same for:
    a. an unqualified nurse
    b. a senior nurse (e.g. a ward manager or sister)
    If not, in what ways is it different?

Child care and flexible working arrangements
Since 90% of the nursing workforce is female, I would now like to ask some questions on child care and flexible working arrangements.

12. Can you tell me about any provisions that have been made for staff nurses (midwives) that require child care?

Probe:
Maternity leave provision: how much?
Workplace child care
Other types of help offered?

13. Are staff nurses (midwives) offered flexible working arrangements?

Probe provisions for:
Career breaks
Part-time working
Job-share

Employee friendly rostering practices
Other types of flexible working arrangements offered?

14. Are the provisions for child care and flexible working arrangements the same for:
    a. an unqualified nurse?
    b. a senior nurse (e.g. a ward manager/ sister)?
    If not, how are they different?

15. How are nursing staff made aware of these provisions for child care and flexible working arrangements?

Monitoring

16. What is your policy on equal opportunities?

17. How is this policy communicated to all your employees?

18. In concrete terms, what do you do to implement the policy?

Recruitment

Probe:
Are records kept of reasons why candidates were successful/unsuccessful at different stages of the recruitment process?
Do you keep records of appointments by ethnic origin?

Training
Does equal opportunities have implications for existing staff?

Probe:
Do you keep records of training by ethnic groups?

Staff appraisals

Probe:
Do you keep a record of appraisals?
Is data available by ethnic origin?
Promotion:

Probe:
Do you keep a record of why candidates where successful/unsuccessful at different stages of the promotion process?
Is this data available by ethnic origin?

19. How often is this data analysed?

Probe:
Who is this data analysed by?
What action has been taken after a review of the data?
Are there 'Local Action Plans' in relation to equal opportunities which are evaluated at the end of a set period?
Review of the procedures and criteria

Appendix 2

SURVEY ON CAREERS OF NURSING STAFF IN THE NHS

The independent POLICY STUDIES INSTITUTE is asking
your views on training, promotion, job satisfaction,
equal opportunities and changes in the NHS.

Please complete this questionnaire as soon as possible
and return it in the envelope provided. Thank you.

POLICY
STUDIES
INSTITUTE

This questionnaire is being sent to nursing staff including qualified nurses and unqualified auxiliaries and assistants. We have used the term 'nurse' throughout the questionnaire to mean all qualified nurses **including midwives and health visitors.** We have used the term 'auxiliary' throughout the questionnaire to mean all unqualified nursing staff including **nursing assistants, nursing auxiliaries, health care assistants and their equivalents.**

Please answer the questions in this questionnaire. Most of the questions can be answered by:

putting a tick in a box, like this .... ☑

or by writing in a number, like this ....*12*.......

HOW YOU STARTED – EVERYONE TO ANSWER

---

1. **How important to you were each of the following in choosing to enter nursing or nursing auxiliary work?**

   PLEASE TICK A BOX IN EACH LINE

	Very important 4	Fairly important 3	Not very important 2	Not at all important 1	
Helping others in the community					8
A job suiting your talents					9
Opportunities for travel					10
Opportunities to take responsibility					11
Opportunities to give supervision					12
Security of employment					13
Prospects of promotion					14
Quality of initial training					15
Prospects of further training					16
Starting salary					17
Long term salary prospects					18
Flexibility of hours of work					19
Status of the job					20
Interesting work					21
Variety of work					22
Rewarding work					23
Family member or friend in nursing					24
Prospects of a career structure					25
Plenty of jobs likely to be available					26
Other reason *(please specify and tick box)*					27

   ....

**ANSWER QUESTIONS 2, 3, 4 AND 5 ONLY IF YOU ARE A *QUALIFIED NURSE;*
UNQUALIFIED STAFF GO TO QUESTION 6**

2. What nursing qualifications have you obtained? Do not include post-basic ENB courses.
   (*Tick ALL that apply*)

   RGN / SRN .... ☐ (28)
   RMN .... ☐ (29)
   RNMH .... ☐ (30)
   RSCN .... ☐ (31)
   EN(G), SEN .... ☐ (32)
   EN(MH) .... ☐ (33)
   RM, SCM .... ☐ (34)
   RHV, HV cert. .... ☐ (35)
   NDN cert. .... ☐ (36)
   RNT .... ☐ (37)
   RCNT .... ☐ (38)
   NNEB .... ☐ (39)
   BA / BSc Nursing .... ☐ (40)
   Other (*please specify and tick box*) .... ☐ (41)
   .... (41-47)

3. In what year did you first register or enrol as a qualified nurse in the UK?

   Please write in year   19 ....   (48-49)
                                                   (50-54)

4. Do you have any overseas nursing qualifications?

                                                   (55)
   Yes .... ☐ 1 **Go to Question 5**
   No .... ☐ 2 **Go to Question 6**

5. How long did it take for you to get registered with the U.K.C.C.?

   .... Years   .... Months   (56-59)

YOUR CURRENT POST – EVERYONE TO ANSWER

6. Is your current post full-time or part-time? (*Please tick ONE box and enter the number of hours for
   part-time*)

                                                   (60)
   Full-time (35 hours or over per week) .... ☐ 1
   Part-time .... ☐ 2
   Job share .... ☐ 3

   If part-time or job share, state hours per week .... hours   (61-62)

7. Which of these categories best describes the specialty of your current post?
(Please tick ONE box only)

(63-64)

Medical/surgical	☐ 1
Paediatric	☐ 2
Midwifery/obstetrics/gynaecology	☐ 3
Mental illness	☐ 4
Mental handicap	☐ 5
Care of the elderly	☐ 6
Health visiting	☐ 7
District nursing	☐ 8
School nursing	☐ 9
Practice nursing	☐ 10
Other *(please specify and tick box)*	☐ 11

....

CAREER HISTORY – EVERYONE TO ANSWER

8. Apart from any period of initial training, in which year did you get your first job as a nurse or nursing auxiliary?

Please write in year   19 ....   (65-66)

9. Have you had any breaks in service? By breaks we mean those periods when you were on maternity leave and periods when you were not employed by the NHS.

(67)

Yes .... ☐ 1

No .... ☐ 2 **Go to Question 13**

10. How many breaks in service have you had altogether?

Please write in number   ....   (68-69)

11. What was the length of the longest break in service?

Please write in number of years and months

.... Years .... Months   (70-73)

(74-80)

3

12. Were you doing any of the following during your breaks of service? *(Please tick ALL that apply)*

(Card 2)

Having or raising a child/ren .... ☐ (10)

Working in some other job .... ☐ (11)

Unemployed and seeking work .... ☐ (12)

Working in nursing abroad .... ☐ (13)

Working in private nursing in the UK .... ☐ (14)

In full or part-time education .... ☐ (15)

Other *(please specify and tick box)* .... ☐ (16-20)

....

13. Including your nurse training, what is the total length of your service to date (not counting any breaks)?

Please write in number of years and months

.... Years .... Months   (21-24)

14. How long have you worked in your present post, that is with your present employer and at your present grade or level (not counting any breaks)?

Please write in number of years and months

.... Years .... Months   (25-28)

(The 1988 regrading does *not* count as a new post. If your employer became a Trust, this does *not* count as a new post.)

15. Do you have any other paid work, apart from your main job?

(29)

Yes .... ☐ 1

No .... ☐ 2 **Go to Question 17**

16. What are these other jobs? *(Please tick ALL that apply)*

NHS nursing .... ☐ (30)

Bank nursing .... ☐ (31)

Agency nursing .... ☐ (32)

Non-NHS nursing .... ☐ (33)

Other job where nursing qualifications are relevant .... ☐ (34)

Job unrelated to nursing .... ☐ (35)

4

17. **What is your pattern of work at present?** *(Please tick ONE box only)*

(36-37)

Mix of earlies, lates and nights	☐ 1
Days only - '9 - 5' or equivalent	☐ 2
Days only - '9 - 3', school hours	☐ 3
Nights only	☐ 4
Mix of earlies and lates	☐ 5
Earlies only	☐ 6
Lates only	☐ 7
Evenings/twilight shift	☐ 8
Split shifts	☐ 9
Flexi time	☐ 10
Other *(please specify and tick box)*	☐ 11

....

18. **What pattern of work would you prefer?** *(Please tick ONE box only)*

(38-39)

Mix of earlies, lates and nights	☐ 1
Days only - '9 - 5' or equivalent	☐ 2
Days only - '9 - 3', school hours	☐ 3
Nights only	☐ 4
Mix of earlies and lates	☐ 5
Earlies only	☐ 6
Lates only	☐ 7
Evenings/twilight shift	☐ 8
Split shifts	☐ 9
Flexi time	☐ 10
Other *(please specify and tick box)*	☐ 11

....

19. **Do you work on a duty roster?**

(40)

Yes	☐ 1
No	☐ 2 **Go to Question 21**

20. **When the duty rosters are being drawn up, how much influence do you have about when you will have time off?** *(Please tick ONE box only)*

(41)

A great deal	☐ 4
Quite a bit	☐ 3
Not much	☐ 2
None at all	☐ 1

21. **If on a particular day you wanted to swap your times of duty with another nurse/auxiliary of the same grade, would your manager or supervisor usually agree?** (*Please tick ONE box only*)

(42)

Always .... ☐ 4

Usually .... ☐ 3

Sometimes .... ☐ 2

Never .... ☐ 1

Not applicable .... ☐ 0

ONLY *HEALTH VISITORS* TO ANSWER – OTHERS GO TO QUESTION 23

22. **If on a particular day you wanted to swap a clinic with another health visitor of the same grade, would your manager or supervisor usually agree?** (*Please tick ONE box only*)

(43)

Always .... ☐ 4

Usually .... ☐ 3

Sometimes .... ☐ 2

Never .... ☐ 1

(44-45)

EVERYONE TO ANSWER

23. **Did you work any extra hours last week?**

(46)

Yes .... ☐ 1

No .... ☐ 2 **Go to Question 26**

---

24. **How many extra hours did you work last week?** (*Please write in number of hours below*)

.... Hours   (47-48)

25a. **Do you expect to be paid for these extra hours, or take time 'in lieu', or both, or neither?**

(49)

Paid .... ☐ 3 **Answer Question 25b**

Time in lieu .... ☐ 2

Both .... ☐ 1 **Answer Question 25b**

Neither .... ☐ 0

b. **How many hours do you expect to be paid for?**

.... Hours   (50-51)

6

GRADING – EVERYONE TO ANSWER

26. What is your grade or equivalent (i.e. A to I)?

Please write in grade   Grade . . . .   (52)

27. Do you think that your current grade is a fair reflection of the duties and responsibilities you have at work?

(53)

Yes . . . . ☐ 1

No . . . . ☐ 2

28. Were you in NHS employment as a nurse or auxiliary at the time of the regrading in October 1988?

(54)

Yes . . . . ☐ 1

No . . . . ☐ 2 **Go to Question 32**

29. Have you appealed against your job grade since you were first informed of your new grade (October 1988)?

(55)

Yes . . . . ☐ 1 **Go to Question 31**

No . . . . ☐ 2

30. Did you ever consider appealing against your job grade?

(56)

Yes . . . . ☐ 1 **Go to Question 32**

No . . . . ☐ 2 **Go to Question 32**

31. What was the outcome of the appeal? (*Please tick ONE box only*)

(57)

Awaiting outcome . . . . ☐ 1

Unsuccessful . . . . ☐ 2

Successful . . . . ☐ 3

Partially successful . . . . ☐ 4

(58-60)

NURSING TASKS AND SATISFACTION – EVERYONE TO ANSWER

32. In your opinion how often, if at all, do you do work which should be undertaken by a lower grade of staff? (*Please tick ONE box only*)

(61)

Daily . . . . ☐ 4

Weekly . . . . ☐ 3

Monthly . . . . ☐ 2

Never . . . . ☐ 1

33. In your opinion how often, if at all, do you do work which should be undertaken by a higher grade of staff? *(Please tick ONE box only)*

(62)

Daily . . . . □ 4

Weekly . . . . □ 3

Monthly . . . . □ 2

Never . . . . □ 1

---

34. Are you a fieldwork teacher/practical workteacher of students or other staff?

(63)

Yes . . . . □ 1

No . . . . □ 2

---

35. Are you a mentor of students or other staff?

(64)

Yes . . . . □ 1

No . . . . □ 2

---

36. Are you a qualified assessor of students or other staff?

(65)

Yes . . . . □ 1

No . . . . □ 2

---

37. Are you at present 'acting up' to a higher grade post?

(66)

Yes . . . . □ 1

No . . . . □ 2

---

38. Are you at present adopting an 'extended role' in your present grade?

(67)

Yes . . . . □ 1

No . . . . □ 2

---

39. Other than anything you have already mentioned, do you have any other management responsibilities for staff?

(68)

Yes . . . . □ 1

No . . . . □ 2

(69-80)

40. How satisfied are you with the following in your present post?

(Card 3)

PLEASE TICK ONE BOX IN EACH LINE	Satisfied 4	Neither satisfied nor dis-satisfied 3	Dissatisfied 2	Very dissatisfied 1	
Your basic pay					(10)
Your present workload					(11)
The amount of auxiliary support available					(12)
The amount of qualified nurse support available					(13)
The amount of administrative/clerical work you have to do					(14)
The amount of time you have for clinical nursing duties					(15)
Your security of employment					(16)
The amount of training opportunities available					(17)
Your involvement in decision making					(18)
Your promotion prospects					(19)
The opportunity to work the hours you want					(20)
Relations with colleagues					(21)
Relations with patients/clients					(22)
Overall, how satisfied are you with your present post					(23)

(24-25)

WORKING ON THE NURSE BANK

THIS SECTION IS FOR QUALIFIED AND UNQUALIFIED NURSING STAFF *WITH A PERMANENT POST WHO ALSO WORK ON THE NURSING BANK*

41. Bearing in mind that you have a permanent post, what are your reasons for also working on the nursing bank? Please indicate how important the following reasons are.

	Very important 4	Fairly important 3	Not important 2	Not at all important 1	
Earning extra money					(26)
Quicker way of gaining varied nursing experience					(27)
It is easier to fit my bank work around my studies					(28)
Unable to get a permanent post in preferred specialty					(29)
It is easier to fit my bank work around my childcare arrangements					(30)

42. How many hours have you worked on the nursing bank in the last four weeks?

Please write in number of hours .... (31-33)

43. **Which of these categories best describes the specialty you usually work in on the nursing bank?**
(Please tick ALL that apply)

Medical / surgical	☐ (34)
Paediatric	☐ (35)
Midwifery / obstetrics / gynaecology	☐ (36)
Mental illness	☐ (37)
Mental handicap	☐ (38)
Care of the elderly	☐ (39)
Health visiting	☐ (40)
District nursing	☐ (41)
School nursing	☐ (42)
Practice nursing	☐ (43)
Other *(please specify and tick box)*	☐ (44-50)

....

---

44. **What is your grade when you work for the nursing bank?**

Please write in grade   ....   (51)

---

45. **Do you think this grade is a fair reflection of the duties and responsiblities you have when working for the nursing bank?**

(52)

Yes .... ☐ 1

No .... ☐ 2

---

46. **Given the choice, would you prefer more paid hours in your permanent post rather than work on the nursing bank?**

(53)

Yes .... ☐ 1

No .... ☐ 2

Don't know .... ☐ 0

47a. **Do you think that black, Asian and white nurses get offered a fair share of work on the nursing bank?**

(54)

Yes .... ☐ 1 **Qualified staff go to Question 48**
Unqualified staff to to Question 58

No .... ☐ 2 **Go to Question 47b**

b. **If no, which group do you think is most often unfairly treated?**

(55)

White nurses .... ☐ 1

Black or Asian nurses .... ☐ 2

10

48a. Have you ever completed or are you currently on any post-basic clinical training courses for a recordable qualification? (i.e. those courses run by the English National Board)

DO NOT INCLUDE ENROLLED TO REGISTERED NURSE CONVERSION COURSES
(Please tick ALL that apply)

Completed course/s .... ☐ (56)

Currently on course/s .... ☐ (57)

Neither .... ☐ (58)   **Go to Question 49**

b. How many of these post-basic recordable qualifications do you have in total?

Please write in number   ....   (59-60)

c. Have you ever applied to go on one of these courses?

(61)

Yes .... ☐ 1

No .... ☐ 2

49. On the whole, is it easy or difficult for you *to get information* on courses for nurses on your grade while you are at work? *(Please tick ONE box)*

(62)

Very easy .... ☐ 5

Fairly easy .... ☐ 4

Neither easy nor difficult .... ☐ 3

Fairly difficult .... ☐ 2

Very difficult .... ☐ 1

50. On the whole, is it easy or difficult for you *to get paid time off* to go on courses?
(Please tick ONE box)

(63)

Very easy .... ☐ 5

Fairly easy .... ☐ 4

Neither easy nor difficult .... ☐ 3

Fairly difficult .... ☐ 2

Very difficult .... ☐ 1

51. On the whole, is it easy or difficult for you *to get the fees of a course paid* for by your employer?
(Please tick ONE box)

(64)

Very easy .... ☐ 5

Fairly easy .... ☐ 4

Neither easy nor difficult .... ☐ 3

Fairly difficult .... ☐ 2

Very difficult .... ☐ 1

52. On the whole, does management encourage you to go on post-basic training courses, like ENB courses for instance, or does it discourage you from going on them? *(Please tick ONE box only)*

          (65)

Encourages a lot .... ☐ 5

Encourages a bit .... ☐ 4

Neither encourages or discourages .... ☐ 3

Discourages a bit .... ☐ 2

Discourages a lot .... ☐ 1

ANSWER QUESTION 53 IF YOU ARE AN *ENROLLED OR SENIOR ENROLLED NURSE;* OTHERWISE GO TO QUESTION 65

---

53. Have you ever applied for a conversion course to become a registered nurse?

          (66)

Yes .... ☐ 1

No .... ☐ 2 **Go to Question 56**

---

54. Were you successful in obtaining a place on the course?

          (67)

Yes .... ☐ 1

No .... ☐ 2 **Go to Question 56**

---

55. Were you seconded by your employer?

          (68)

Yes .... ☐ 1 **Go to Question 65**

No .... ☐ 2 **Go to Question 65**

---

56. Do you intend to apply for a conversion course (either again or for the first time) in the next twelve months?

          (69)

Yes .... ☐ 1

No .... ☐ 2

---

57. On the whole, does management encourage you to apply for a conversion course or does it discourage you from applying?

          (70)

Encourages a lot .... ☐ 5

Encourages a bit .... ☐ 4

Neither encourages or discourages .... ☐ 3

Discourages a bit .... ☐ 2

Discourages a lot .... ☐ 1

58. Have you ever applied to undertake basic nurse training?

(71)

Yes .... ☐ 1

No .... ☐ 2

59a. Have you completed any work-related training courses that lead to an NVQ?

(72)

Yes .... ☐ 1 **Go to Question 59b**

No .... ☐ 2 **Go to Question 59c**

b. At what level of NVQ are you qualified?

(73)

NVQ I .... ☐ 1

NVQ II .... ☐ 2

Higher level .... ☐ 3

c. Are you currently on a work-related training course that leads to an NVQ?

(74)

Yes .... ☐ 1

No .... ☐ 2

---

60. Do you have any overseas nursing qualifications?

(75)

Yes .... ☐ 1

No .... ☐ 2

---

61. On the whole, does management encourage you *to go on further training courses* or does it discourage you from going on them? *(Please tick ONE box only)*

(76)

Encourages a lot .... ☐ 5

Encourages a bit .... ☐ 4

Neither encourages or discourages .... ☐ 3

Discourages a bit .... ☐ 2

Discourages a lot .... ☐ 1

13

62. On the whole, is it easy or difficult for you *to get information on courses* for auxiliaries on your grade while you are at work? *(Please tick ONE box only)*

(77)

Very easy	☐ 5
Fairly easy	☐ 4
Neither easy nor difficult	☐ 3
Fairly difficult	☐ 2
Very difficult	☐ 1

63. On the whole, is it easy or difficult for you *to get paid time off* to go on training courses? *(Please tick ONE box only)*

(78)

Very easy	☐ 5
Fairly easy	☐ 4
Neither easy nor difficult	☐ 3
Fairly difficult	☐ 2
Very difficult	☐ 1

64. On the whole, is it easy or difficult for you *to get the fees of a course paid* for by your employer? *(Please tick ONE box only)*

(79)

Very easy	☐ 5
Fairly easy	☐ 4
Neither easy nor difficult	☐ 3
Fairly difficult	☐ 2
Very difficult	☐ 1

CHILDCARE AND WORKING ARRANGEMENTS – EVERYONE TO ANSWER

65. Do you have any children under the age of 16?

(80)

Yes	☐ 1
No	☐ 2 **Go to Question 69**

66. How many of your children are under the age of 16? *(Please write in how many where appropriate)*

(Card 4)

How many of your children are aged 0-5?	. . . .	(10)
How many of your children are aged 6-16?	. . . .	(11)

14

67. Some employers give help of various kinds to parents of children up to age 16. Have you made use of any of the following with your present employer? *(Please tick ALL that apply)*

Flexible full-time working hours .... ☐ (12)

Job-sharing .... ☐ (13)

Career-break or retainer schemes .... ☐ (14)

Special shifts (e.g. evenings for parents) .... ☐ (15)

Assistance in funding child-care facilities away
from the workplace .... ☐ (16)

Financial help for the costs of child-care
(e.g. child-care vouchers) .... ☐ (17)

Facilities at the workplace for looking after young children
(e.g. creche, nursery) .... ☐ (18)

Holiday playscheme .... ☐ (19)

Other arrangements *(please specify and tick box)* .... ☐ (20-25)

....

68. In general, how good are the facilities your employer provides for parents like you with children up to the age of 16? *(Please tick ONE box only)*

(26)

Very good .... ☐ 5

Fairly good .... ☐ 4

Neither good nor bad .... ☐ 3

Fairly bad .... ☐ 2

Very bad .... ☐ 1

(27-30)

THE FUTURE – EVERYONE TO ANSWER

69. What do you expect to be doing in three years from now? *(Please tick ALL that apply)*

Nursing job in the private sector .... ☐ (31)

Better NHS nursing job (higher grade or preferred speciality) . ☐ (32)

Same nursing job and grade as present .... ☐ (33)

Same nursing job and lower grade than present .... ☐ (34)

Non-nursing job .... ☐ (35)

Full or part-time education .... ☐ (36)

Raising a family .... ☐ (37)

Nursing job overseas .... ☐ (38)

Non-nursing job overseas .... ☐ (39)

Retired .... ☐ (40)

Redundant .... ☐ (41)

Unemployed .... ☐ (42)

Other *(please specify and tick box)* .... ☐ (43-47)

....

Don't know .... ☐ (48)

15

GENERAL EDUCATION – EVERYONE TO ANSWER

70a. Do you have any of the qualifications listed below?

(49)

Yes .... ☐ 1 **Answer Question 70b**

No .... ☐ 2

b. If yes, please fill in how many you have.

How many?

CSE or equivalent

Grade 1 .... (50-51)

Grade 2-5 .... (52-53)

GCSE or equivalent

Grade A, B or C .... (54-55)

Grade D, E, F or G .... (56-57)

GCE O level or equivalent

Grades A, B or C, or pass before 1975 .... (58-59)

Grades D or E .... (60-61)

GCE A level

A level or Higher School Certificate or Matric .... (62)

ONC, OND, BEC, TEC, BTEC - National or General
Certificate or Diploma .... (63)

HNC, HND, BEC, BTEC, TEC - Higher Certificate or
Higher Diploma .... (64)

Teaching qualification .... (65)

University Diploma .... (66)

First Degree (eg. BA, BSc) .... (67)

Higher Degree (eg. MSc, PhD) .... (68)

---

71. Are you studying for a degree at present?

(69)

Yes .... ☐ 1

No .... ☐ 2

---

72. Apart from any ENB courses, are you studying for a diploma at present?

(70)

Yes .... ☐ 1

No .... ☐ 2

BACKGROUND INFORMATION – EVERYONE TO ANSWER

73. What year were you born?

Please write here   19 ....   (71-72)

74. Are you:

(73)

Male .... ☐ 1

Female .... ☐ 2

75. Are you: *(Please tick ONE box only)*

(74)

Married or living together .... ☐ 1

Single / widowed / divorced or separated .... ☐ 2

76. Are you currently living in: (Please tick ONE box only)

(75)

Privately owned accommodation .... ☐ 1

Privately rented accommodation .... ☐ 2

NHS accommodation .... ☐ 3

Council accommodation .... ☐ 4

Housing Association accommodation .... ☐ 5

Other *(please specify and tick box)* .... ☐ 6-9

....

77. Are you a member of a trade union or professional association?

(76)

Yes .... ☐ 1

No .... ☐ 2 **Go to Question 79**

78. Which trade union or professional association do you belong to? *(Please tick ALL that apply)*

(Card 5)

UNISON (NALGO/NUPE/COHSE) .... ☐ (10)

RCN .... ☐ (11)

RCM .... ☐ (12)

HVA / MSF .... ☐ (13)

DNA .... ☐ (14)

CPNA .... ☐ (15)

Other *(please specify and tick box)* .... ☐ (16-20)

....

17

79. In what country were you born?

(21-22)

United Kingdom & N. Ireland	☐ 1
Eire/Irish Republic	☐ 2

Caribbean

West Indies/Guyana	☐ 3

Indian Sub-Continent

India	☐ 4
Pakistan	☐ 5
Bangladesh	☐ 6
Sri Lanka	☐ 7

African Continent

Africa	☐ 8
Mauritius	☐ 9

Asia

Philippines	☐ 10
Hong Kong	☐ 11
Singapore	☐ 12
China	☐ 13
Vietnam	☐ 14
Malaysia	☐ 15

Australasia

New Zealand	☐ 16
Australia	☐ 17
Other country *(please specify and tick box)*	☐ 18

....

**ONLY ANSWER QUESTION 80 *IF YOU WERE NOT BORN IN THE UNITED KINGDOM;*
OTHERWISE GO TO QUESTION 81**

---

80. *If you were not born in the United Kingdom,* how old were you when you moved to **Britain?**

Please write here   .... Years   (23-24)

18

81. Would you describe your ethnic origins as: *(Please tick ALL that apply)*

White .... ☐ (25)

Black Caribbean .... ☐ (26)

Indian Caribbean .... ☐ (27)

Black African .... ☐ (28)

Black other *(please specify and tick box)* .... ☐ (29-34)

....

Indian .... ☐ (35)

Pakistani .... ☐ (36)

Bangladeshi .... ☐ (37)

Chinese .... ☐ (38)

Other *(please specify and tick box)* .... ☐ (39-44)

....

EQUAL OPPORTUNITIES – EVERYONE TO ANSWER

82a. Do you think that applicants are ever refused nursing jobs *in the NHS* for reasons to do with their race or colour, and if so how often do you think this happens? *(Please tick ONE box only)*

(45)

No, never .... ☐ 1

Rarely .... ☐ 2 Go to Question 82b

Occasionally .... ☐ 3 Go to Question 82b

Fairly often .... ☐ 4 Go to Question 82b

Often .... ☐ 5 Go to Question 82b

b. Do you think this happens mainly to:

(46)

White nurses .... ☐ 1

Black or Asian nurses .... ☐ 2

Both .... ☐ 3

83a. Do you think that applicants are ever refused nursing jobs *in your workplace* for reasons to do with their race or colour, and if so how often do you think this happens? *(Please tick ONE box only)*

(47)

No, never .... ☐ 1

Rarely .... ☐ 2 Go to Question 83b

Occasionally .... ☐ 3 Go to Question 83b

Fairly often .... ☐ 4 Go to Question 83b

Often .... ☐ 5 Go to Question 83b

b. Do you think this happens mainly to:

(48)

White nurses .... ☐ 1

Black or Asian nurses .... ☐ 2

Both .... ☐ 3

84a. Do you think that nursing staff *in the NHS* are ever denied the opportunity to go on training courses for reasons to do with their race or colour, and if so how often do you think this happens? *(Please tick ONE box only)*

(49)

No, never .... ☐ 1

Rarely .... ☐ 2 **Go to Question 84b**

Occasionally .... ☐ 3 **Go to Question 84b**

Fairly often .... ☐ 4 **Go to Question 84b**

Often .... ☐ 5 **Go to Question 84b**

b. Do you think this happens mainly to:

(50)

White nurses .... ☐ 1

Black or Asian nurses .... ☐ 2

Both .... ☐ 3

85a. Do you think that nursing staff in your workplace are ever denied the opportunity to go on training courses for reasons to do with their race or colour, and if so how often do you think this happens? *(Please tick ONE box only)*

(51)

No, never .... ☐ 1

Rarely .... ☐ 2 **Go to Question 85b**

Occasionally .... ☐ 3 **Go to Question 85b**

Fairly often .... ☐ 4 **Go to Question 85b**

Often .... ☐ 5 **Go to Question 85b**

b. Do you think this happens mainly to:

(52)

White nurses .... ☐ 1

Black or Asian nurses .... ☐ 2

Both .... ☐ 3

---

86. While working in the NHS, have you yourself ever been refused a job for reasons to do with your race or colour, and if so when did this last happen? *(Please tick ONE box only)*

(53)

No, never .... ☐ 1

Within the past year .... ☐ 2

Within the past five years .... ☐ 3

Over five years ago .... ☐ 4

---

87. While working in the NHS, have you yourself ever been refused a promotion for reasons to do with your race or colour, and if so when did this last happen? *(Please tick ONE box only)*

(54)

No, never .... ☐ 1

Within the past year .... ☐ 2

Within the past five years .... ☐ 3

Over five years ago .... ☐ 4

88. While working in the NHS, have you yourself ever been refused a training opportunity for reasons to do with your race or colour, and if so when did this last happen? *(Please tick ONE box only)*

(55)

No, never .... ☐ 1

Within the past year .... ☐ 2

Within the past five years .... ☐ 3

Over five years ago .... ☐ 4

89. Do patients or their families ever behave towards you in a difficult, aggressive or hostile way for reasons to do with your race or colour, and if so how often does this happen?
(Please tick ONE box only)

(56)

No, never .... ☐ 1

Daily .... ☐ 2

Weekly .... ☐ 3

Monthly .... ☐ 4

Less often .... ☐ 5

90. Do members of the nursing staff (including supervisors or managers) ever behave towards you in a difficult, aggressive or hostile way for reasons to do with your race or colour, and if so how often does this happen? *(Please tick ONE box only)*

(57)

No, never .... ☐ 1

Daily .... ☐ 2

Weekly .... ☐ 3

Monthly .... ☐ 4

Less often .... ☐ 5

91. Does your employer have a policy of ensuring equal opportunities for people from all racial or ethnic groups? *(Please tick ONE box only)*

(58)

Yes .... ☐ 1

No .... ☐ 2 **Go to Question 93**

Don't know .... ☐ 3 **Go to Question 93**

92. How effective do you think it is? *(Please tick ONE box only)*

(59)

Very effective .... ☐ 4

Fairly effective .... ☐ 3

Not very effective .... ☐ 2

Not effective at all .... ☐ 1

93. *In the regrading of 1988,* do you think that white and ethnic minority nursing staff were treated equally, or that one or other group was given much better or somewhat better treatment? *(Please tick ONE box only)*

(60)

White and ethnic minority nursing staff given equal treatment	1
Ethnic minority staff given much better treatment	2
Ethnic minority staff given somewhat better treatment	3
White staff given much better treatment	4
White staff given somewhat better treatment	5
Don't know	6

94. On the whole, do you think that ethnic minorities and white people have *equal chances in nursing in the NHS,* or that one or other group has much better or somewhat better chances? *(Please tick ONE box only)*

(61)

White and ethnic minority people have equal chances	1
Ethnic minorities have much better chances	2
Ethnic minorities have somewhat better chances	3
White people have much better chances	4
White people have somewhat better chances	5
Don't know	6

95. Finally, please use the space below for any other comments you would like to make about any of the questions we have asked you.

....
....
....
....
....

We would like to contact you again in a year's time to find out how your career has progressed and whether you are still in nursing. To enable us to contact you, would you please write your name, home address and telephone number below.

....
....
....

This information will be used only to contact you again in connection with this study.

Thank you very much for your help. Now please post the questionnaire in the enclosed stamped addressed envelope. All your answers will be treated IN COMPLETE CONFIDENCE.

Appendix 3   Unweighted response data

Table A.1   **Unweighted data: Place of birth of NHS nursing staff (based on 1991 census classifications)**

Place/area of birth	Number	Per cent
Great Britain & N. Ireland	11,737	82
Eire/Republic of Ireland	629	4
European Community (excluding UK & Ireland)		
Germany	56	<1
Spain	28	<1
Italy	10	<1
Remainder of Europe		
Poland	2	<1
Old Commonwealth		
Australia	35	<1
New Zealand	22	<1
Canada	12	<1
USA	15	<1
African-Caribbean (including New Commonwealth)		
West Indies/Guyana	602	4
Africa	290	2
Asia (including New Commonwealth)		
Malaysia	147	1
India	95	1
Philippines	80	1
Sri Lanka	50	<1
Singapore	32	<1
Hong Kong	28	<1
Pakistan	15	<1
Bangladesh	2	<1
Vietnam	1	<1
China	6	<1
Remainder of New Commonwealth		
Mauritius	190	1
Cyprus	18	<1
Malta	9	<1
Other		
Other	138	1
Not stated	91	1
Total nursing staff	14,330	100

Table A.2   Unweighted data: Ethnic origin of NHS nursing staff

Ethnic origin	Number	Per cent
White	11,705	82
Black Caribbean	572	4
Indian	257	2
Black African	212	2
Chinese	182	1
Indian Caribbean	82	<1
Mauritian	72	<1
Filipino	47	<1
Other	104	<1
Pakistani	34	<1
Sri Lankan	30	<1
Bangladeshi	10	<1
Black other	119	1
Not stated	995	7
Total nursing staff	14,421	

The total of nurses is 14,330, so some have answered two categories.

Appendix 4

Technical report on the multivariate analyses

Background

This part of the report on nursing staff's careers was intended to build on the descriptive results from the postal survey. To summarise, the descriptive results suggested that although their grades were comparable, there were differences in the situations of staff from different ethnic minority groups. For example, ethnic minority staff were overrepresented in certain specialties.

In addition, ethnicity was associated with a range of variables that themselves might be associated with nursing progress, such as age, length of time in the profession, and general educational qualifications.

The logistic regression procedure had two stages:

- to find out which variables were significantly associated with nursing level, and then

- to control for them and look to see whether ethnicity had any further explanatory power over and above the effect that it had already had on those variables.

Logistic regression

Logistic regression is a form of multivariate analysis (that is, it involves more than two variables) where the dependent or response variable is dichotomous (1either/or). Logistic regression can be used to predict the probability or odds that a person has a given characteristic (for example, have they reached grade D or higher?) based on a combination of independent or predictor variables. The predictor variables can also be dichotomous (like male/female), or they can be continuous (like age). The probability of a nurse or midwife having reached any particular grade will always be between 0 and 1, where 0 means she will not, and 1 means she will. Logistic regression produces odds-ratio estimates for each independent factor in the equation, rather than the least squares estimates produced by usual multiple regression techniques. Odds measure the ratio of the probability that a characteristic will be present to the probability that it will be absent. Odds of 1, for example, indicate an even chance that a characteristic will be present.

In multivariate procedures such as logistic regression, a whole range of independent variables can be held constant to allow us to estimate the

273

influence of one particular variable, such as ethnicity in this case. However, to do this ethnicity itself must be broken down into a series of dichotomous variables where each different ethnicity is compared to a 'reference' group. In these analyses, the different ethnicities are compared to the white group. In other words, white nursing staff's chances of reaching certain grades were the base line against which the chances of ethnic minority nursing staff were compared. Thus, we can derive an estimate of the probability of reaching a certain grade if you are black, versus if you are white, holding everything else that might vary constant, such as age, educational qualifications, specialty, etc.

The following statistics are presented for the independent variables in the models:

Beta coefficient: When the independent variable is dichotomous (such as black/white) the beta coefficient indicates the extent to which a change (for example, from white to black) affects the outcome (log odds of reaching a certain grade). When the independent variable is continuous (for example, general education score), the beta coefficient estimates the degree of change in the outcome (log odds of reaching a certain grade) associated with a one unit increase in the independent variable. When the beta coefficient is positive, the odds are increased. When it is negative, the log odds are lowered.

Exponential of the beta coefficient: Similarly, this measures the factor by which the odds of reaching a certain grade are changed when a given variable either changed from the reference category to the observed category (from white to black, for example) or increased by one unit (of general education, for example). A factor of one means that the odds were unchanged, a factor of more than one means they were increased, and less than one means they were decreased.

Statistical significance: The changes in the dependent variable might just be the result of chance and so statistical tests are done to check that the probability that the effects seen are more likely to have arisen than we might expect by chance. The minimum level of significance usually taken is 0.05, where the results might have arisen by chance in five cases out of 100. The test (WALD) is actually done on the basis of factors not seen in these tables (such as the standard error) so sometimes things that look as if they should be significant are not & vice versa.

Chi-square for goodness of fit: Also presented is a test of how much each individual independent variable improves the statistical model. This is the best test of the relative weights of the different variables in terms of their predictive power. This is derived by entering all the variables in the model, then taking out the one of interest, and looking at the difference this makes to the overall fit. This is presented as a chi-square statistic and its significance is also presented. It is another way of looking at what is most important. Variables that have much higher chi-square values are those that significantly improve the model.

The tables below present the results for the final six models, where all variables already shown to be significant are included in order of the size of their contribution, and the additional predictive power of ethnicity is assessed. The models were estimated using the logistic regression procedure available in SPSSX, and variables were entered according to the FSTEP (forward step) method. Observations were weighted to correct for sampling bias, and the weights rescaled so that the total number of observations matched the original number of respondents.

Model 1 Reached grade C or above

Variables	Beta coefficient	Exponential	Chi-Sq
Nursing qualifications	5.2461	189.82***	12550.47***
Time in nursing	.0100	1.01***	80.67***
Age	-.0618	.94***	55.56***
Sector overall			10.87***
Sector - lower status	-.2112	.81 (n/s)	
Sector - midwife etc	-.7325	.48**	
Sector - Primary hc	.3254	1.38 (n/s)	
(reference medical)			
Constant	-2.3809		

The fit of the model (-2*Log Likelihood) was 1557.445 with a likelihood ratio x^2 of 12697.521 (df=13804), p>.999.

Significance

***	p.<001
**	p.<01
*	p.<0.5
a/s	approaching sifnificance
n/s	not significant (p>.08)

Model 2   Reached grade D or above

Variables	Beta coefficient	Exponential	Chi-Sq
Nursing qualifications	1.9729	7.19***	1423.66***
Sector overall	59.72***		
Sector - lower status	.4487	1.57**	
Sector - midwife etc	-.3445	.71 (n/s)	
Sector - Primary hc (reference medical)	1.3230	3.75***	
Time in nursing	.0031	1.003***	25.85***
Sex	.8901	2.43*	9.62***
Constant	-1.8156		

The fit of the model (-2*Log Likelihood) was 2203.061 with a likelihood ratio x^2 of 1518.851 (df=10809), p>.999.

Significance

***	p.<001
**	p.<01
*	p.<0.5
a/s	approaching sifnificance
n/s	not significant (p>.08)

Model 3   Reached grade E or above

Variables	Beta coefficient	Exponential	Chi-Sq
Nursing qualifications	1.6215	5.06***	3738.94***
Time in	.0075	1.18**	917.57***
Sector overall	464.36***		
Sector - lower status	.6124	1.84***	
Sector - midwife etc	1.3130	3.71***	
Sector - Primary hc	1.6990	5.47***	
(reference medical)			
General education score	.1656	1.18***	41.55***
Age	.0111	1.01**	7.60***
Ethnicity overall	12.39***		
Ethnicity - Black	-.1848	.83 (n/s)	
Ethnicity - Asian	.3899	1.48*	
Ethnicity - Other	.5822	1.79*	
Ethnicity - Not stated	.1383	1.15 (n/s)	
(reference white)			
Constant	-6.2792		

The fit of the model (-2*Log Likelihood) was 7519.318 with a likelihood ratio x^2 of 5182.418 (df=10804), p>.999.

Significance

***	p.<001
**	p.<01
*	p.<0.5
a/s	approaching sifnificance
n/s	not significant (p>.08)

Model 4   Reached grade F or above

Variables	Beta coefficient	Exponential	Chi-Sq
Nursing qualifications	1.6155	5.03***	2723.61***
Sector overall	1838.01***		
Sector - lower status	.2071	1.24*	
Sector - midwife etc	.8510	2.34***	
Sector - Primary hc (reference medical)	2.8242	16.85***	
Time in nursing	.0074	1.007***	1100.87***
Working part-time (reference full-time)	-.8459	.43***	215.01***
General education	.2140	1.23***	102.08***
Age	.0338	1.03***	58.39***
Ethnicity overall	22.54***		
Ethnicity - Black	-.6497	.52***	
Ethnicity - Asian	-.3180	.73 (a/s)	
Ethnicity - Other	.0251	1.03 (n/s)	
Ethnicity - Not stated (reference white)	-.1620	.85 (n/s)	
Sex	.3262	1.38 ***	10.79 ***
Constant	-9.1116		

The fit of the model (-2*Log Likelihood) was 8740.092 with a likelihood ratio x^2 of 6071.377 (df=10801), p>.999.

Significance

***	p.<001
**	p.<01
*	p.<0.5
a/s	approaching sifnificance
n/s	not significant (p>.08)

Model 5   Reached grade G or above

Variables	Beta coefficient	Exponential	Chi-Sq
Sector overall	1471.77***		
Sector - lower status	.2100	1.23*	
Sector - midwife etc	.8271	2.28***	
Sector - Primary hc	2.3246	10.22***	
(reference medical)			
Nursing qualifications	1.2323	3.43***	1512.77***
Time in nursing	.0063	1.006***	931.51***
Working part-time	-1.2796	.28***	466.57***
(reference full-time)			
General education	.2715	1.31***	171.23***
Age	.0414	1.04***	82.22***
Ethnicity overall	25.38***		
Ethnicity - Black	-.6689	.51***	
Ethnicity - Asian	-.2147	.81 (n/s)	
Ethnicity - Other	.1067	1.11 (n/s)	
Ethnicity - Not stated	-.2268	.80*	
(reference white)			
Sex	.4073	1.50***	16.14***
Constant	-8.7588		

The fit of the model (-2*Log Likelihood) was 8494.705 with a likelihood ratio x^2 of 4677.604 (df=10801), p>.999.

Significance

***	p.<001
**	p.<01
*	p.<0.5
a/s	approaching sifnificance
n/s	not significant (p>.08)

Model 6   Reached grade H or above

Variables	Beta coefficient	Exponential	Chi-Sq
Time in nursing	.0057	1.005***	346.97***
General education	.3603	1.43***	25.49***
Working part-time (reference full-time)	-1.6867	.18***	332.61***
Nursing qualifications	.8330	2.30***	218.31***
Sector overall	60.26***		
Sector - lower status	-.4729	.62***	
Sector - midwife etc	-.6972	.49***	
Sector - Primary hc (reference medical)	.2038	1.23 (a/s)	
Age	.0394	1.04***	34.84***
Sex	.5867	1.80***	21.37***
Constant	-8.8994		

The fit of the model (-2*Log Likelihood) was 3716.677 with a likelihood ratio x^2 of 1155.341 (df=10805), p>.999.

Significance

***	p.<001
**	p.<01
*	p.<0.5
a/s	approaching sifnificance
n/s	not significant (p>.08)

Index